The Open University

S197
How the Universe works

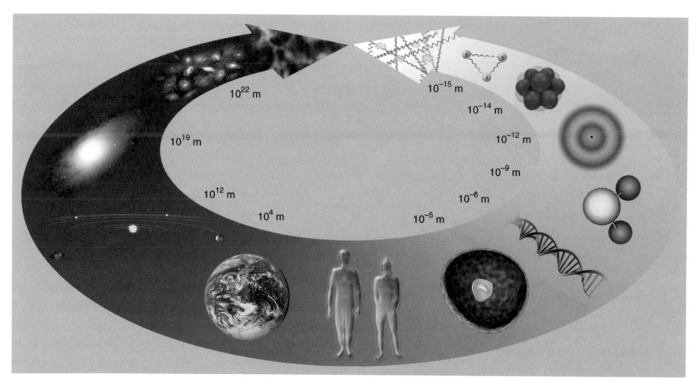

People stand midway between the immensity of the Universe and the unimaginable smallness of atomic nuclei and their building blocks. Yet what happened long ago involving these tiniest objects set the entire Universe on its course. Today, we cannot understand the Universe as a whole without understanding Nature on the smallest scales. That is why the largest and the smallest meet in this picture. (Courtesy Canopus Publishing Limited. Reproduced from *Nucleus, A Trip into the Heart of Matter*. Mackintosh et al., 2001)

The S197 Course Team

Chair and Author	Andrew Norton
Course Assessor	David Wands (University of Portsmouth)
Readers	Stuart Freake, Janet Humphreys
Course Manager	Isla McTaggart
Science Short Course Programme Director	Elizabeth Whitelegg
Editor	Dick Sharp
Multimedia Developer	Greg Black
Graphic Designer	Jenny Nockles
Graphic Artist	Steve Best
Indexer	Jane Henley

This course is based on Block 11 *Universal Processes* of the Open University course S103 *Discovering Science*. Several members of the S103 course team made such a substantial contribution to the design, content and style of *Universal Processes* that their influence has carried over into this course. We particularly acknowledge the contributions of the following people: David Broadhurst, Stuart Freake, Isla McTaggart, Andrew Norton, Rebecca Graham, Pam Owen, Howard Taylor, Mark Jones, Fiona Thomson, Anne-Marie Gallen, Claire Horrobin, Marie Jefsioutine, Ian Thomas, Darren Wycherley and Andrew Liddle (University of Sussex).

This publication forms part of an Open University course, S197 *How the Universe works*. Details of this and other Open University courses can be obtained from the Course Information and Advice Centre, PO Box 724, The Open University, Milton Keynes MK7 6ZS, United Kingdom: tel. +44 (0)1908 653231, e-mail general-enquiries@open.ac.uk

Alternatively, you may visit the Open University website at www.open.ac.uk, where you can learn more about the wide range of courses and packs offered at all levels by The Open University.

To purchase a selection of Open University course materials visit the webshop at www.ouw.co.uk, or contact Open University Worldwide, Michael Young Building, Walton Hall, Milton Keynes MK7 6AA, United Kingdom, for a brochure: tel. +44 (0)1908 858785; fax +44 (0)1908 858787; e-mail ouwenq@open.ac.uk

The Open University
Walton Hall, Milton Keynes
MK7 6AA

First published 2003. Reprinted 2005

Copyright © 2003 The Open University

Edited, designed and typeset by The Open University.

Printed and bound in the United Kingdom by The Alden Group, Oxford.

ISBN 0 7492 5851 9

1.2

Contents

1

The Universe

The purpose of life is the investigation of the Sun, the Moon, and the heavens.

Anaxagoras, 59 BC

I am very interested in the Universe – I am specializing in the Universe and all that surrounds it…

Peter Cook, 1937–1995

Understanding how the Universe works is surely the ultimate subject that can be addressed by science. Other scientific issues, such as global warming or genetic engineering, may have more immediate relevance to our everyday lives, but when it comes to fundamental questions like

- How does the Universe appear today?
- What rules does the Universe follow?
- How did the Universe get to be as it is?

there are simply none bigger. Answers to questions such as these are to be found in the fields of **cosmology** and **particle physics**. Scientists who work in these two apparently unrelated areas of science — one concerned with the infinitely large, the other with the unimaginably small — have come together in recent years in an attempt to understand the Universe. This book explores the realms of cosmology and particle physics and shows how ideas found there enable us to investigate the origin and evolution of the Universe and so explain how the Universe works.

1.1   Cosmology and particle physics

Cosmology is the branch of science that involves the study of the Universe as a whole. The research tools of cosmologists include powerful telescopes, such as those in Figure 1, which are able to detect galaxies out to the farthest reaches of the Universe. You can get a flavour of this work later by using a computer-based 'virtual telescope' to measure the expansion rate of the Universe, and so measure its age. It may seem strange that people working in this field should count particle physicists amongst their closest allies. The research tools of particle physicists include giant particle accelerators, such as that shown in Figure 2, in which high-energy beams of particles are smashed together, enabling details of exotic reactions to be investigated and understood. But this is the key to the union of these two subjects. For only in particle accelerators are scientists able to recreate the high-energy conditions that filled the Universe during the first moments of its existence. When particle physicists study these reactions they can provide cosmologists with a window on the Universe when it was only one-thousandth of a billionth of a second old.

An example of the interplay between these two areas of study concerns the fundamental particles known as neutrinos. A few years ago, cosmologists announced that there can be no more than three 'flavours' (or types) of neutrino. If there were four, say, then they calculated that there would be more helium in the Universe than is actually observed, as a result of particle reactions that occurred in the early Universe. Particle physicists, studying decays of exotic particles in their high-energy accelerators, were also able to calculate how many types of neutrino there are in the Universe. The answer the particle physicists arrived at was also three — if there were

Figure 1 The twin domes of the W. M. Keck Observatory, 4200 m above sea-level on the summit of Mauna Kea, Hawaii. These huge domes each house a telescope whose primary mirror is 10 m in diameter. When they were completed in 1997 these telescopes were the largest in the world, enabling astronomers to observe objects up to 250 million times fainter, and see detail on a scale 500 times finer, than can be seen with the naked eye.

Figure 2 The Large Hadron Collider (LHC) at CERN, the European Laboratory for Particle Physics near Geneva in Switzerland. The LHC consists of a ring 27 km in circumference, within which two high-energy beams of particles will collide head-on. When completed in 2005 it will enable particle physicists to recreate conditions that existed only one thousandth of a billionth of a second after the Big Bang.

more, or fewer, flavours of neutrino, the particles under study would have decayed at a different rate. So we can be fairly confident that there really are only three types of neutrino in the Universe — whether the problem is tackled from the large or the small scale.

The important idea is that cosmology and particle physics complement each other. They are two research areas at the forefront of scientific understanding, and we hope that you will find learning about them to be both stimulating and rewarding. Some of the ideas discussed here may challenge the view of the world that you currently hold, and throughout history such challenges have been one of the hallmarks of scientific progress. Apart from the intellectual excitement of these topics, they serve to illustrate the way in which scientists continually strive to push back the boundaries of knowledge, starting from what can be measured in the laboratory and leading to realms that are impossible to study directly. You'll also encounter some pretty bizarre ideas in the following pages! From fundamental particles a billion times smaller than an atom, to the expanding infinite Universe, the range of length-scales is almost unimaginable. You'll discover particles that appear out of nothing, gravitational waves that permeate the entire Universe and an ultimate theory of everything that implies we live in an 11-dimensional space–time. Prepare to exercise your mental muscles as we embark on a journey to the frontiers of physics and an exploration of the fundamental processes that govern the Universe.

1.2   A route-map for understanding how the Universe works

We'll take the three big questions outlined at the start of Chapter 1 and use these as our themes for what follows.

In the first part of the book, comprising Chapters 2 to 4, we'll be concerned with the overall *structure* and *composition* of the Universe and how they have changed throughout time. We'll begin by examining the components of matter that comprise the world around us. Taking the world apart, we first examine atoms, then look at their nuclei, and finally look inside the protons and neutrons to discover quarks – the fundamental building blocks of the Universe. On the very largest scales, the Universe is not static — it was different in the past from how it is now, and it will be different again in the future. Our understanding of this evolution relies crucially on two pieces of evidence: first, evidence that the Universe is *expanding* and, second, evidence that the Universe is *cooling*. We examine each of these in turn to complete our picture of the Universe today.

Any attempt to chart the history of our evolving Universe must take account of the laws that govern all physical processes. Accordingly, the second part of the book, in Chapters 5 to 8, contains accounts of the distinctive features of the four types of interaction of all matter and radiation: electromagnetic, strong, weak and gravitational. Chapter 9 presents a short detour from our main theme to examine how the four types of interaction each play a part in the life of our local power station – the Sun. Then in Chapter 10, the question is raised as to whether the four interactions are truly distinct or whether there might be bigger and better theories, unifying two or more of the four interactions.

Bringing together the information from the first ten chapters, the final part of the book, in Chapters 11 and 12, presents a history of the Universe, from the earliest times of which one can meaningfully speak, through the present day, and into the distant future.

This book contains most of the material that you will need for the course, but there are a number of other computer-based *activities* described here also. Embedded within Chapter 3 is an activity entitled 'The virtual telescope'. Using your computer, you will take measurements of galaxies from which you will be able to measure the expansion rate of the Universe and so calculate its age. Chapter 9 ends with a video activity 'Seeing inside the Sun', which shows how observations of our nearest star are used to understand the fundamental processes occurring deep within its interior. Finally, Chapter 11 contains another computer package, 'A history of the Universe' that presents an interactive exploration of the evolving cosmos.

There is very little maths in this book, and no algebra. In particular, whenever we need to use an equation, we simply explain it in words, rather than using complicated symbols. Box 1, *Numbers: very large and very small*, is the first of three boxes in the book that are designed to help you deal with the sorts of numbers you will encounter here.

Box 1 Numbers: very large and very small

When discussing the Universe, it is frequently necessary to refer to very large and very small numbers. Scientists and mathematicians have developed a short hand way of writing such numbers for convenience. The easiest way to demonstrate this is with a few examples.

(a) Large numbers

First, a few simple ones:

$100 = 10 \times 10$ and is written as 10^2 (pronounced 'ten to the power two')

$1000 = 10 \times 10 \times 10$ and is written as 10^3 ('ten to the power three')

$1\,000\,000 = 10 \times 10 \times 10 \times 10 \times 10 \times 10$ and is written as 10^6 ('ten to the power six')

So the power to which the number 10 is raised (sometimes called the **index** or **exponent**) is simply the number of times 10 is multiplied by itself to make the number in question. More complicated numbers can also be written in a similar way. For instance

$3456 = 3.456 \times 10 \times 10 \times 10$ and is written as 3.456×10^3

$987\,000 = 9.87 \times 10 \times 10 \times 10 \times 10 \times 10$ and is written as 9.87×10^5

The last two examples are said to be written in **scientific notation**: that is, as a number between 1 and 10, multiplied by 10 raised to some power. To enter such a number into your calculator will generally involve a button labelled 'E' or 'EXP' (standing for 'exponent'). So the example above would be entered as: ③ ⎡·⎤ ④ ⑤ ⑥ EXP ③. Make sure you know how to enter numbers in scientific notation into your own calculator.

Another useful way of describing large numbers is by using the following prefixes:

kilo (k) = 10^3;   mega (M) = 10^6;   giga (G) = 10^9

For instance, you will be familiar with the idea that 1000 metres (10^3 m) is one kilometre (1 km). Other units of measurement may also be prefixed by these terms to indicate larger quantities. Finally, we will also sometimes refer to the number 10^9 as a **billion.**

(b) Small numbers

So much for large numbers, but what about small numbers? Well, it turns out that small numbers can be treated in a similar way. Again, a few simple examples to start with:

$0.1 = 1/10$ and is written as 10^{-1} ('ten to the power minus one')

$0.01 = 1/(10 \times 10)$ and is written as 10^{-2} ('ten to the power minus two')

$0.000\,01 = 1/(10 \times 10 \times 10 \times 10 \times 10)$ and is written as 10^{-5} ('ten to the power minus five')

More complicated numbers can also be written in a similar way. For instance:

$0.987 = 9.87/10$ and is written as 9.87×10^{-1}

$0.000\,034\,56 = 3.456/(10 \times 10 \times 10 \times 10 \times 10)$ and is written as 3.456×10^{-5}

Once again, these small numbers are written in scientific notation because they are given as a number between 1 and 10 multiplied by 10 raised to some power, in this case a negative index or exponent. Make sure you know how to enter numbers in scientific notation with negative exponents into your calculator too. If in doubt, refer to your calculator's operating manual.

There are also a few prefixes that are useful for describing very small numbers, namely:

milli (m) = 10^{-3};   micro (µ)= 10^{-6};   nano (n) = 10^{-9}

Notice that the symbol for micro is the Greek letter *mu*, simply because the letter m is already used for the prefix milli. As an example of the use of these prefixes, you will no doubt be familiar with the fact that one-thousandth of a metre (10^{-3} m) is one millimetre (1 mm). Other units of measurement may also be prefixed by these terms to indicate smaller quantities.

(c) Combining large and small numbers

The use of powers of ten often makes it easier to carry out calculations too. This is because, when doing multiplication or division, the powers of ten are simply added or subtracted respectively. As usual, some examples will illustrate this. First, multiplication:

$10^4 \times 10^3 = 10^{(4+3)} = 10^7$ (i.e. $10\,000 \times 1000 = 10\,000\,000$)

$10^5 \times 10^{-3} = 10^{(5-3)} = 10^2$ (i.e. $100\,000 \times 0.001 = 100$

$10^{-2} \times 10^3 = 10^{(-2+3)} = 10^1$ (i.e. $0.01 \times 1000 = 10$)

and also division:

$10^4/10^3 = 10^{(4-3)} = 10^1$ (i.e. $10\,000/1000 = 10$)

$10^5/10^{-3} = 10^{5-(-3)} = 10^8$ (i.e. $100\,000/0.001 = 100\,000\,000$)

$10^{-2}/10^3 = 10^{(-2-3)} = 10^{-5}$ (i.e. $0.01/1000 = 0.000\,01$)

Question 1

(a) Arrange the following numbers in order of increasing size:

10^{-4}, 10^4, 3×10^{-4}, 3×10^4, 10^{-3}, 3×10^{-3}

(b) How many times bigger than 10^{23} is 10^{25}?   *100*

(c) Express a distance of 300 m in both millimetres and kilometres. ◀

3×10^5 mm 3×10^{-1} km

Question 2

Work out the following multiplications and divisions involving large and small numbers (without using a calculator!):

$10^8 \times 10^5$; $10^9 \times 10^{-4}$; $10^{-11} \times 10^{-6}$; $10^9/10^3$; $10^7/10^{12}$; $10^{-4}/10^{-13}$ ◀

10^{13} ; 10^5 ; 10^{-17} ; 10^6 ; 10^{-5} ; 10^7

PART I
How does the Universe appear today?

The structure and contents of our local patch of the Universe are reasonably familiar to many people (Figure 3). The Earth is a rather small, rocky, body and is one of several planets that orbit our local star, the Sun. The Sun itself is a fairly average star, about 5 billion years old and mid-way through its life. It is just one of a hundred billion or so stars that comprise our Galaxy, known as the Milky Way. Our Galaxy itself takes the form of a flattened spiral structure, with the Sun lying in one of the outer spiral arms, about two-thirds of the way from the centre to the edge. Finally, our Galaxy is merely one of several dozen which comprise the Local Group of galaxies, and the Local Group is itself part of the much larger Local Supercluster of galaxies, which may contain around a hundred thousand individual galaxies.

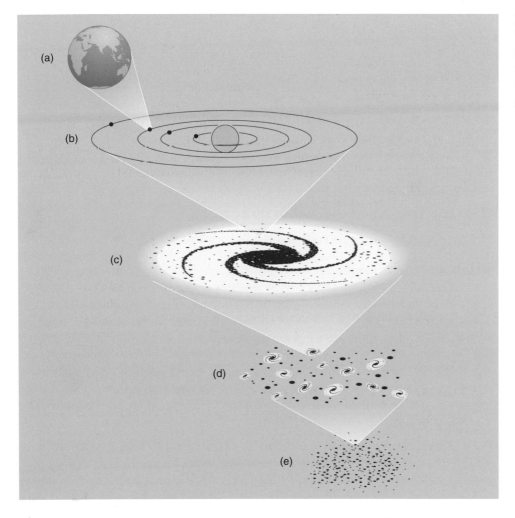

Figure 3 Our place in the Universe: (a) The Earth; (b) the Solar System; (c) the Milky Way; (d) the Local Group of galaxies; (e) the Local Supercluster of galaxies.

In the following three chapters, we investigate different aspects of the way the Universe appears today. First, we look at the matter content of the Universe and examine how the world around us may be broken down into its smallest fundamental components. We then look at how the Universe is moving on its largest scales as we consider the expanding Universe. Finally, we consider the radiation content of the Universe and examine how the Universe is gradually cooling.

Taking the Universe apart

The most incomprehensible thing about the Universe is that it is comprehensible.

Albert Einstein, 1879–1955

2.1 Atoms and nuclei

Everything around us is composed of **atoms**, and there are known to be around ninety different types of atom that occur naturally in the world. These different types of atom are known as **elements**. The Universe as a whole is mostly composed of the two simplest types of atom: the elements hydrogen and helium. Later in the book, you will see just why this is the case. Here on Earth, there are also significant amounts of other elements, in particular carbon, nitrogen, oxygen, sodium, magnesium, aluminium, silicon, sulfur, calcium and iron. Later on, you will find out where these elements came from too.

Some substances in the world around us exist in the form of pure elements. Diamond, for example, contains only carbon atoms arranged in a rigid structure. Other substances take the form of **chemical compounds**. For instance, common salt, or sodium chloride, comprises crystals containing both sodium and chlorine atoms. In gases or liquids, atoms may combine together to form discrete **molecules**. You probably know, for instance, that the chemical symbol for carbon dioxide is CO_2. This indicates that a carbon dioxide molecule is composed of one carbon atom and two oxygen atoms. Similarly, ammonia has the chemical symbol NH_3 – the molecule contains one atom of nitrogen and three hydrogen atoms.

nucleons eg neutron proton

⬤ Of what atoms is a water molecule (H_2O) composed?

○ One oxygen atom and two hydrogen atoms.

atom

Whatever the type of atom, each one has certain features in common. Each contains a central **nucleus**, which carries a positive **electric charge** as well as most of the atom's mass. The nucleus is surrounded by one or more negatively charged particles known as **electrons** (symbol: e⁻) each of which has a much lower mass than the nucleus. The nucleus of an atom is what determines the type of element. The very simplest atoms of all, those of the element hydrogen, have a nucleus consisting of just a single particle, known as a **proton** (symbol: p). The next simplest atom, helium, has two protons in its nucleus; lithium has three protons; beryllium has four; boron five; carbon six; and so on. The *number* of protons in the nucleus of an atom is known as its **atomic number.**

eg. Hydrogen atom protons have nucleus of 1 particle called proton

When speaking of the value of electric charge of particles and atoms, it is most convenient to use that of a proton as the reference point. So, the electric charge of a proton is said to be '+1' unit. The electric charge of an electron is exactly the same as that of a proton, but negative instead of positive. The electric charge of an electron is therefore '−1' unit.

⬤ What is the atomic number of carbon? What is the electric charge of a carbon nucleus?

○ As noted above, the nucleus of a carbon atom contains six protons, so the atomic number of carbon is 6 and the charge of the nucleus is +6 units.

The other constituents of atomic nuclei are particles known as **neutrons** (symbol: n). Neutrons have a similar mass to that of protons, but have zero electric charge. They therefore contribute to the mass of an atom, but not to its electric charge. Normal hydrogen atoms do not have neutrons in their nuclei, although there is a form of hydrogen – known as deuterium – that does. The nucleus of a deuterium atom consists of a proton and a neutron. It is still the element hydrogen (since it contains only one proton) but it is a 'heavy' form of hydrogen, thanks to the extra neutron. Deuterium is said to be an **isotope** of hydrogen. Similarly, normal helium atoms contain two neutrons in their nucleus, along with the two protons; but a 'light' isotope of helium contains only one neutron instead. The total number of protons *and* neutrons in the nucleus of an atom is known as the **mass number** of the atom.

⬤ What are the mass numbers of (a) normal hydrogen, (b) 'heavy' hydrogen (i.e. deuterium), (c) normal helium, and (d) 'light' helium?

◯ (a) The nucleus of normal hydrogen contains one proton, so the mass number is 1. (b) The nucleus of deuterium contains one proton and one neutron so the mass number is 2. (c) The nucleus of normal helium contains two protons and two neutrons, so the mass number is 4. (d) The nucleus of 'light' helium contains two protons and one neutron, so the mass number is 3.

As a shorthand, isotopes of each atomic element may be represented by a symbol. Letters are used to indicate the name of the element itself, and two numbers are used to indicate the atomic number (lower) and mass number (upper). Hence a normal hydrogen atom is represented as $^{1}_{1}H$, and an atom of the heavier isotope, deuterium, by $^{2}_{1}H$. Isotopes of some other light atoms are indicated in Table 1 and Figure 4.

Table 1   Some isotopes of the eight lightest elements. Isotopes of the same element have the same atomic number but different mass number. Some isotopes are unstable, that is they decay to other products.

Atomic number	Mass number	Isotope name	Isotope symbol
1	1	hydrogen	$^{1}_{1}H$
	2	deuterium	$^{2}_{1}H$
2	3	helium-3	$^{3}_{2}He$
	4	helium-4	$^{4}_{2}He$
3	7	lithium-7	$^{7}_{3}Li$
4	7	beryllium-7 (unstable)	$^{7}_{4}Be$
	8	beryllium-8 (unstable)	$^{8}_{4}Be$
	9	beryllium-9	$^{9}_{4}Be$
5	11	boron-11	$^{11}_{5}B$
6	12	carbon-12	$^{12}_{6}C$
	13	carbon-13	$^{13}_{6}C$
	14	carbon-14 (unstable)	$^{14}_{6}C$
7	14	nitrogen-14	$^{14}_{7}N$
8	16	oxygen-16	$^{16}_{8}O$

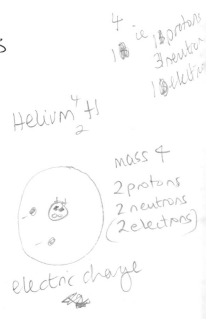

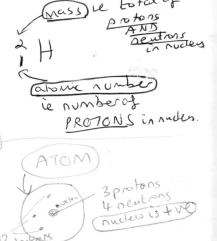

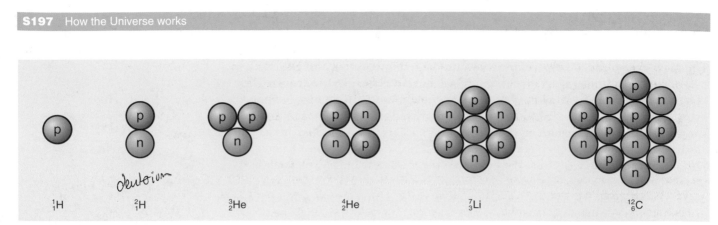

deutoion

$^1_1$H $\quad$ $^2_1$H $\quad$ $^3_2$He $\quad$ $^4_2$He $\quad$ $^7_3$Li $\quad$ $^{12}_6$C

Figure 4 Schematic diagrams of the nuclei of some isotopes. Protons are coloured red, and neutrons green.

Sometimes, protons and neutrons are collectively referred to as **nucleons** since both types of particle reside inside the nucleus of an atom. Similarly, electrons, protons and neutrons are often collectively referred to as **subatomic** particles, for obvious reasons. This nomenclature is summarized in Table 2.

Table 2 The constituents of atoms.

	Subatomic particles	
electron $\quad$ e⁻	*nucleons*	
	mass number = total number of nucleons	ie protons + neut
	proton p	**neutron** n
In a neutral atom, number of electrons = number of protons	*atomic number* = total number of protons	*isotopes* of the same element have different numbers of neutrons
electric charge = −1 unit	electric charge = +1 unit	electric charge = 0

Normal atoms are electrically neutral. That is to say, the positive electric charge of the nucleus is exactly balanced by the negative electric charge of the electrons surrounding it. Since each electron carries an electric charge of −1 unit and each proton carries an electric charge of +1 unit, the number of electrons in a neutral atom is *exactly* the same as the number of protons in its nucleus.

○ What is the difference between an atom of lithium-7 and an atom of beryllium-7?

○ Both atoms have the same mass number, namely 7. However, the nucleus of the lithium atom has three protons and four neutrons, whilst the nucleus of the beryllium atom has four protons and three neutrons. Furthermore, the lithium atom contains three electrons whilst the beryllium atom contains four electrons.

$^7_3$Li lithium -7

$^7_4$Be beryllium -7

Whereas a typical atomic nucleus has a size of around 10^{-14} m, the size of the atom itself is determined by the size of the region occupied by the electrons that surround the nucleus. The overall size of an atom is about 10^{-10} m across.

○ How much larger than a nucleus is an atom? Think of some everyday examples of things with these relative sizes.

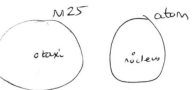

An atom is about $(10^{-10}/10^{-14}) = 10^4$ times larger than the nucleus. The continent of Australia is roughly 4000 km across. An atom this size would have a nucleus only 400 m across, about the size of a city block. The M25 ring road around London has a diameter of order 40 km. If an atom was this size, the nucleus would be only 4 m across, or the size of a taxi in central London.

For a number of years at the beginning of the 20th century it was believed that the electrons in an atom travelled around the nucleus following orbits, in much the same way as planets orbit the Sun in our Solar System (Figure 5). However, since the 1920s it has been known that this *cannot* be correct – the true situation is far stranger!

It is now known that electrons in atoms exist in a 'fuzzy cloud' around the nucleus. This picture is predicted by a so-called **quantum** theory of the atom and has been verified experimentally. The cloud is fuzzy because it is *impossible* to tell exactly where an electron is at any instant in time. In some sense, each electron is actually in many places at once, and all that can be said is that there is a certain **probability** of each electron being in a particular location with a particular speed. An **electron probability cloud** for the single electron in a hydrogen atom is shown in Figure 6. The cloud is dense in those regions where there is a high probability of finding the electron, and sparse in those regions where the electron is unlikely to be found. One way of thinking about such a cloud is as follows. Imagine that you could perform an experiment to measure the position of the electron within a hydrogen atom. If you did this ten thousand times, and each time drew a dot at the location where you found the electron to be, the result would be something like Figure 6. Of course, this is only a two-dimensional drawing of the real three-dimensional situation, but it gives the general idea.

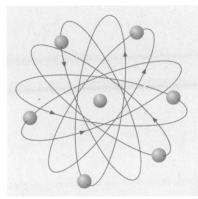

Figure 5   Electrons in orbit around an atomic nucleus. Although conceptually appealing, such a picture has been known to be *false* since the 1920s.

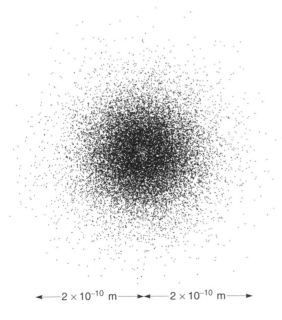

←—— 2×10^{-10} m ——→←—— 2×10^{-10} m ——→

Figure 6   The electron probability cloud for the single electron in a hydrogen atom.

$E = mc^2$

$E \propto m$.

2.2 Mass, energy, matter and antimatter

Before we continue taking the Universe apart, we take a slight detour to examine the concepts of matter and antimatter and the most famous equation in all of physics. If there's one equation in physics which *everyone* has heard of, it's Einstein's favourite: $E = mc^2$ (read as 'ee equals em cee squared', see Figure 7). What Einstein tells us via this equation is that energy (E) and mass (m) are interchangeable. Energy may be converted into mass and mass may be converted into energy. The conversion factor linking the two is the speed of light squared (c^2).

"Now that desk looks better. Everything's squared away, yessir, squaaaaaared away."

Figure 7 The most famous equation in all of physics.

Mass is a physical property that quantifies the amount of matter in a body. If, for simplicity, we consider an object, such as a diamond, that is composed entirely of carbon atoms, then a more massive diamond will contain more atoms of carbon than a less massive diamond does.

Energy is a physical property possessed by an object that measures its capacity to make changes to other objects. There are a variety of possible changes, and these include changes in speed of motion, changes in temperature and changes in position with respect to other massive or electrically charged objects. Perhaps the most familiar form of energy is **kinetic energy**, or energy of movement. The more massive a moving object, or the faster it is moving, the greater is its kinetic energy. Some other types of energy fall into the category of **potential energy**, namely energy that is stored and which depends on the position of an object. Potential energy is so called because it gives an object the *potential* to make changes to other objects. Gravitational energy is one form of potential energy that is possessed by a massive object as a result of its separation from other massive objects. When an object is dropped, its gravitational potential energy is converted into kinetic energy as it speeds towards the ground. Electrical energy is also a form of potential energy, in this case possessed by an electrically charged object as a result of its separation from other electrically charged objects. Electromagnetic radiation, such as light, also carries energy, as you will see in Chapter 3.

When dealing with atoms and subatomic particles, the most convenient unit to use for energy is the **electronvolt** (symbol: eV). It's not too important exactly how big an electronvolt is, the key point is that it happens to be the right sort of size to describe the energies we're interested in. Now, because of the interchangeability of mass and energy, it is also convenient to refer to the masses of subatomic particles in terms of their energy equivalence. For instance, the energy equivalent of the mass of an electron is around 500 keV (500 kiloelectronvolts or 500 000 electronvolts) and the energy equivalent of the mass of either a proton or neutron is around 1 GeV (one gigaelectronvolt, or one billion electronvolts). The term **mass energy** is often used to refer to this energy equivalent of the mass of a particle. A summary of the mass energies of the electron, proton and neutron is given in Table 3 for reference.

Table 3 Mass energies of the constituents of atoms. [You don't have to remember details of all these particles — they are summarized on the Bookmark.]

Particle	Mass energy
proton (p)	1 GeV
neutron (n)	1 GeV
electron (e⁻)	500 keV

[handwritten annotations: electron Volt eV. ; 10^9 eV, 1000,000,000 eV + 500,000 = 1,000,500,000 ; 5×10^5 eV]

○ Given the information above, how much more massive than an electron is a proton?

○ The mass energy of a proton is 1 GeV or 10^9 eV, and the mass energy of an electron is 500 keV or 5×10^5 eV. The ratio of these two energies is $(10^9/5 \times 10^5) = 2000$, so a proton is about 2000 times more massive than an electron.

Two particular ways in which mass and energy are converted from one into the other are via the processes of pair creation and matter–antimatter annihilation. Although you may have thought **antimatter** to be the stuff of science fiction, it is a very real feature of the Universe. Antimatter particles have the same mass as their matter counterparts but their other attributes, such as electric charge, have the opposite sign. All matter particles have corresponding antimatter counterparts. Our Universe today seems to consist almost exclusively of matter particles rather than antimatter. However, as you will see later, the early Universe was not such a one-sided place.

The antimatter counterpart of the electron, the **positron**, was discovered in 1932. More recently, in 1996, atoms of antihydrogen were created, each consisting of one antiproton bound to one positron. Nowadays, antimatter particles can be created routinely in high-energy particle accelerators, but it is difficult stuff to control! If matter and antimatter come into contact with each other they will mutually annihilate, producing a large amount of energy, which appears in the form of electromagnetic radiation. The process of **matter–antimatter annihilation** may therefore be expressed as:

matter + antimatter → electromagnetic radiation

The process of **pair creation** is exactly the reverse:

electromagnetic radiation → matter + antimatter

[handwritten: electron antimatter is the positron]

One of the most important rules governing how the Universe works is that:

☾ Energy cannot be created or destroyed, but merely *changed* from one form to another.

So, for instance, any amount of kinetic energy, electrical energy, gravitational energy, mass energy, or energy of electromagnetic radiation may be converted into exactly the same amount of any other type of energy. This is known as the **principle of** conservation of energy, and it appears to be a fundamental property of the Universe. Notice that this principle implicitly *includes* mass energy as a form of energy, just like any other.

In the annihilation and pair creation reactions, we have to be careful though, because there are *two* types of energy to consider when talking about matter and antimatter. First, there's the mass energy of the various matter and antimatter particles, and in addition to this, there's the kinetic energy possessed by the particles as well. So, in annihilation reactions, the energy of the electromagnetic radiation that is produced is equal to the mass energy of the matter and antimatter particles *plus* their combined kinetic energy. Similarly, in pair creation reactions, the energy of the electromagnetic radiation can appear as the mass energy of the matter and antimatter particles, and any energy left over is imparted to the particles as kinetic energy.

● An electron and a positron *at rest* annihilate each other. How much energy is carried by the electromagnetic radiation that is created?

○ The electron and positron each have a mass energy of about 500 keV (Table 3). Because they are at rest, their kinetic energy is zero. The total energy available is therefore 2×500 keV, so the energy carried by the electromagnetic radiation is 1 MeV.

● If a proton and an antiproton are created from high-energy electromagnetic radiation, what is the *minimum* energy that the radiation must have?

○ A proton and an antiproton each have a mass energy of about 1 GeV (Table 3), so the radiation must have an energy of at least 2 GeV. If the electromagnetic radiation had more than 2 GeV of energy, then the excess energy would appear as kinetic energy of the proton and antiproton.

2.3 Leptons and quarks

Half a century ago, the account of what the Universe is made of would have ended here. But now a third layer of structure is known beyond that of atoms and nucleons: it is believed that protons and neutrons are composed of structureless particles known as quarks. In this section we will be looking at an area that is at the forefront of scientific research today. Our aim is nothing less than an understanding of the fundamental constituents from which the Universe is built.

Radioactive decay processes have been known about since the end of the 19th century, from the work of scientists such as Henri Becquerel, Ernest Rutherford and Marie Curie. One type of radioactive decay process is known as **beta-decay**. In a beta-decay, an atomic nucleus *changes* from one type of element to another. The atomic number of the nucleus either increases or decreases by one, but the mass number remains the same. In the process, a beta-particle is emitted.

● How could the atomic number of a nucleus increase or decrease by one, but the mass number remain the same?

○ One of the protons could turn into a neutron or vice-versa.

By the 1930s it had become clear that, as well as the beta-particles being emitted in beta-decay, something else must also be coming out of the nucleus and carrying away some of the energy. Beta-particles were soon identified as simply fast-moving electrons, and the mysterious 'something else' was eventually recognized as being an entirely new type of particle — a **neutrino.** In fact, in beta-minus decay, the emitted electron (e⁻) is accompanied by an **electron antineutrino** (given the rather clumsy symbol $\bar{\nu}_e$); whereas in the rarer beta-plus decay, a positron is emitted (e⁺) accompanied by an **electron neutrino** (ν_e). This illustrates the first of many patterns that emerge in subatomic physics: particles created in beta-decays are always emitted as a matter–antimatter pair.

[handwritten: see page 76]

Electrons (e⁻) and electron neutrinos (ν_e), together with their antiparticles, are believed to be fundamental particles. By fundamental, we mean that there is no evidence that they are composed of smaller or simpler constituents. Furthermore, two more particles, with the same charge as the electron only rather heavier, were discovered in 1936 and 1975. The first is known as the muon (represented by μ^- — the Greek letter *mu*, rhymes with 'cue'), which is about 200 times heavier than the electron. The second is called the tauon (represented by τ^-— the Greek letter *tau*, rhymes with 'cow'), which is about 3500 times heavier than the electron. The superscript minus signs on the symbols for the electron, muon and tauon indicate that these particles have negative electric charge. Like the electron, the muon and tauon each has an associated neutrino: the muon neutrino (ν_μ) and the tauon neutrino (ν_τ).

These six fundamental particles are collectively referred to as **leptons** — they are listed in Table 4 along with their electric charge. (The word lepton comes from the Greek *leptos* meaning 'thin' or 'lightweight'.) The six different types are often rather whimsically referred to as different **flavours** of lepton, and the three pairs of particles are often referred to as three **generations** of leptons.

Table 4 Six flavours of lepton. [You don't have to remember details of all these particles — they are all summarized on the Bookmark.]

	1st generation	2nd generation	3rd generation
leptons with charge − 1 unit *[charged leptons −ve]*	e⁻ *electron*	μ⁻ *muon*	τ⁻ *tauon*
leptons with charge 0 units *[neutrino leptons Ø charge]*	ν_e *electron neutrino*	ν_μ *muon neutrino*	ν_τ *tau neutrino*

To each lepton there corresponds an **antilepton** with opposite charge but with the same mass. These are denoted by the symbols e⁺, μ⁺ and τ⁺ for the charged leptons, and $\bar{\nu}_e, \bar{\nu}_\mu$ and $\bar{\nu}_\tau$ for the neutral leptons.

The other subatomic particles that you have so far met — protons and neutrons — are examples of **hadrons**. (The word hadron comes form the Greek *hadros*, meaning 'strong' or 'robust'.) Although the *only* hadrons existing around us in the everyday world are protons and neutrons, many more types of hadron can be created in high-energy collisions. Such reactions are common in the upper atmosphere, where high-energy cosmic-ray protons collide with nuclei of nitrogen and oxygen, smashing them apart and creating new hadrons. Since the 1960s, such reactions have also been closely studied under controlled conditions, in high-energy physics laboratories.

Although many dozens of different types of hadron may be created in this way, all of the new ones are *unstable* and they rapidly decay into other, long-lived, particles, such as leptons, protons and neutrons. Fortunately, it will not be necessary for you to dwell on (let alone remember) the names and properties of all the types of hadron,

19

other than protons and neutrons. This is because there is a straightforward description for building hadrons from particles that *are* believed to be fundamental, namely from **quarks** and **antiquarks**.

There are six flavours of quark, labelled (for historical reasons) by the letters u, d, c, s, t and b, which stand for up, down, charm, strange, top and bottom. Their charges are listed in Table 5. Like the six leptons, the six quarks are often grouped into three generations, on the basis of their mass, with the first generation quarks being the least massive.

Table 5 Six flavours of quark. [You don't have to remember details of all these particles — they are all summarized on the Bookmark.]

	1st generation	2nd generation	3rd generation
quarks with charge $+\frac{2}{3}$ unit	u *up*	c *charm*	t *top*
quarks with charge $-\frac{1}{3}$ unit	d *down*	s *strange*	b *bottom*

To each quark, there corresponds an antiquark, with the opposite charge and the same mass. These are denoted by $\bar{u}$, $\bar{d}$, $\bar{c}$, $\bar{s}$, $\bar{t}$ and $\bar{b}$.

The **up quarks** and **down quarks** are the constituents of protons and neutrons, and along with their antiquark counterparts are the least massive of all the quarks. The charm and strange quarks and antiquarks are more massive than the up and down quarks, and the top and bottom quarks and antiquarks are more massive still. The large masses of these second- and third-generation quarks are the reason why large particle accelerators are required to produce them. In order to create this amount of mass, a large amount of kinetic energy must be supplied. In fact, hadrons containing top quarks were first detected in the period 1994–5. They have masses nearly 200 times that of the proton.

Quarks and antiquarks have *never* been observed in isolation. They only occur bound together inside hadrons and there are three recipes for building hadrons from quarks, as shown in Figure 8. The net electric charge of a hadron is simply the sum of the electric charges of the quarks or antiquarks of which it is composed, as shown in Box 2, *Adding and subtracting thirds*.

A hadron can consist of:

- three quarks (in which case it is called a **baryon**),
- three antiquarks (in which case it is called an **antibaryon**),
- one quark and one antiquark (in which case it is called a **meson**).

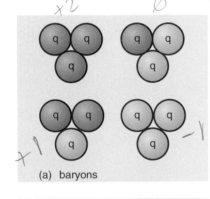

(a) baryons

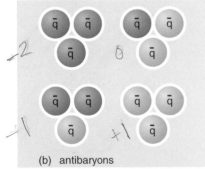

(b) antibaryons

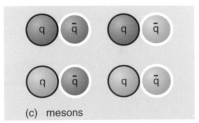

(c) mesons

Figure 8 The three recipes for building hadrons from quarks. Quarks and antiquarks with a charge of ±2/3 unit are shown in purple, those with a charge of ±1/3 unit are shown in orange. The symbol q represents a quark, and $\bar{q}$ represents an antiquark. (a) Possible combinations making a baryon. (b) Possible combinations making an antibaryon. (c) Possible combinations making a meson.

Box 2 Adding and subtracting thirds

In order to work out the electric charge of particles composed of quarks and antiquarks, the *only* thing you have to be able to do is add and subtract in thirds. The way to do this is best illustrated with an example. In order to carry out the following sum:

$$+\frac{2}{3}+\frac{2}{3}+\frac{2}{3}$$

the way to proceed is simply to add or subtract the numbers on the top line: (+2 +2 +2) = 6 and then write this over the bottom line (3) which is the same for all the terms in the sum, i.e.

$$+\frac{2}{3}+\frac{2}{3}+\frac{2}{3}=\frac{6}{3}$$

You should then note that 6 divided by 3 is simply 2, so the final answer is

$$+\frac{2}{3}+\frac{2}{3}+\frac{2}{3}=2$$

Extending this idea to electric charges of composite particles, to calculate the electric charge of a hadron composed of an anti-up quark ($\bar{u}$) and a down quark (d), for instance, we proceed as follows.

The electric charge of an up quark (u) is +2/3 unit

So the electric charge of an anti-up quark ($\bar{u}$) is −2/3 unit

The electric charge of a down quark (d) is −1/3 unit

Therefore the net charge of the composite particle ($\bar{u}$d) is $\left(-\frac{2}{3}-\frac{1}{3}\right)$

The net charge of the composite particle in this case is therefore (−3/3) = −1 unit.

As a specific example of the hadron-building recipe, the proton is a baryon, so it is composed of three quarks, and, as mentioned above, it is composed of up and down quarks only. Now, the proton has charge +1 unit and the only way that three up or down quarks can be combined to make this net charge is by combining two up quarks with a down quark. So the quark content of a proton is (uud), giving a charge

$$\left(+\frac{2}{3}+\frac{2}{3}-\frac{1}{3}\right)=+\frac{3}{3}=+1 \text{ unit.}$$

● A neutron is also a baryon. Following the pattern above, determine its quark content. [Hint: remember the charge of a neutron is zero, and like the proton it too is composed of three up or down quarks.]

● Since the neutron has a charge of zero and is composed of three up or down quarks, its quark content must be (udd), giving a charge +2/3 − 1/3 − 1/3 = 0.

21

A summary of the nomenclature introduced in this chapter is given in Table 6.

Table 6   Fundamental particles.

leptons		quarks	
electron muon tauon electric charge = −1 unit	electron neutrino muon neutrino tauon neutrino electric charge = 0	up, charm, top quarks electric charge – +2/3 unit	down, strange, bottom quarks electric charge = −1/3 unit
		hadrons	
		baryons	**mesons**
		composed of three quarks	composed of quark and antiquark

The tally of six leptons and six quarks, each with their own antiparticles, may seem like a huge number of fundamental particles. However, don't let this put you off. Everything around us is made up of merely the first generation of each type, namely electrons, up quarks and down quarks, with electron neutrinos being created in beta-decays. This slimmed down total of four particles is all that you need to remember. The second generation of leptons (μ^- and ν_μ) and the second generation of quarks (c and s), the third generation of leptons (τ^- and ν_τ) and the third generation of quarks (t and b), have exactly the same properties as their first-generation counterparts, except that they are more massive. Quite why nature decided to repeat this invention three times over is not currently understood.

2.4   Summary and questions

Atoms consist of a positively charged nucleus surrounded by a cloud of negatively charged electrons. Each type of atom is known as an element and is distinguished by its atomic number, which is simply the number of protons in its nucleus, or the number of electrons in the neutral atom. The mass number of an atom is the total number of protons and neutrons in its nucleus. Different isotopes of a particular element have different numbers of neutrons.

Energy can take a variety of forms, including kinetic energy, electrical (potential) energy and gravitational (potential) energy. In all physical processes, energy is conserved. A convenient unit of energy to use when describing atomic processes is the electronvolt (eV).

Mass and energy may be converted from one into the other via the processes of matter–antimatter annihilation and pair creation, according to Einstein's most famous equation. Mass energy may therefore be considered as simply another form of energy.

The mass energy of an electron or a positron is about 500 keV, and the mass energy of a proton or a neutron is about 2000 times larger.

The electron and the electron neutrino are examples of leptons. There are six flavours of lepton in total, all of which are believed to be fundamental, structureless particles. Each lepton has an associated antilepton with the same mass but opposite charge.

There are also six flavours of quark. The least massive are the up quark and the down quark. Quarks, like leptons, are believed to be fundamental particles. Unlike leptons, they have never been observed in isolation. Each quark also has an associated antiquark with the same mass but opposite charge.

Hadrons are composite particles made of quarks and antiquarks. Combinations of three quarks are called baryons, combinations of three antiquarks are called antibaryons, and combinations consisting of a quark and an antiquark are called mesons.

Nucleons (protons and neutrons) are merely special cases of baryons. Protons have the quark composition (uud) and neutrons have the quark composition (udd).

Question 3

The element iron has the atomic number 26, and its most common isotope is known as iron-56. (a) How many protons and how many neutrons are there in a single nucleus of iron-56? (b) How many electrons are there in an electrically neutral atom of iron-56? (c) Roughly, what is the mass energy, in gigaelectronvolts (GeV), of an atom of iron-56? ◀

(a) 26 protons 30 Neutrons

(b) 26 electrons

(c) 56 GeV

Question 4

Antiparticles of the proton and neutron are composed of antiquarks. What are the constituents of (a) an antiproton and (b) an antineutron? In each case calculate the charge of the resulting antiparticle by adding up the charges of the constituent antiquarks. ◀

(a) $\bar{u}\bar{u}\bar{d}$ → $-\frac{2}{3} + -\frac{2}{3} + \frac{4}{3} = -1$

(b) $\bar{u}\bar{d}\bar{d}$ → $-\frac{2}{3} + \frac{1}{3} + \frac{1}{3} = 0$

Question 5

Following the rule for constructing baryons outlined earlier, what are the only possible values of electric charge that a baryon can have? ◀

$2, 0, 1, -1$

Q3. Iron $^{56}_{26}Fe$ 26 protons ⇒ 26 GeV ⎫ = 56 GeV
                          30 neutrons ⇒ 30 GeV ⎬
                          26 electrons
                          ↳ 26 × 500 keV = 13 MeV (negligible)
                          13 000 keV = 13 M

The expanding Universe

Spectrum analysis enabled the astronomer to tell when a star was advancing head on, and when it was going the other way. This was regarded as very precious. Why the astronomer wanted to know, is not stated; nor what he could sell out for, when he did know. An astronomer's notions about preciousness were loose. They were not much regarded by practical men, and seldom excited a broker.

Mark Twain, 1835–1910

The deduction that the Universe is expanding is based on measurements of two quantities for each of thousands of galaxies: their distance away and the speed with which they are moving. Each of these quantities is determined in a quite straightforward manner by applying laws of physics that are tried and tested here on Earth — but applying them to situations on a much larger scale of both distance and time.

In order to make any sense of the observations that will be discussed, it is necessary to assume that the laws of physics that operate in distant parts of the Universe (distant in both time and space) are the *same* as those that operate in laboratories on the Earth, today. In fact, this is only an extreme version of an assumption that underlies the whole of science: we assume that the laws of physics were the same in Birmingham yesterday as they will be in Bangalore tomorrow, for instance. If this were not true, then no further progress would be possible. Conversely, the fact that apparently sensible conclusions can be reached by making just this one assumption, tends to indicate that it is not such a bad assumption after all. If such assumptions were to lead to inconsistencies with observations, then we would have to re-examine the original assumptions and possibly modify the laws of physics as they are currently expressed. This process is the essence of the *scientific method*.

● When trying to discover the properties of a distant galaxy, what is the only thing that astronomers can actually measure that comes from the galaxy in question?

○ The only thing that can be measured is the *light* (or other electromagnetic radiation such as radio waves or X-rays) emitted by the galaxy. So essentially the only knowledge astronomers can have about a distant galaxy comes from measurements of this radiation.

When the light from a galaxy is collected using telescopes, different types of measurement can be made on it. The simplest measurement is to determine how *bright* the galaxy appears to be, that is how much light emitted by the galaxy is detected here on Earth. A slightly more complex measurement is to examine the *spectrum* of the light emitted by the galaxy. As you will see in the rest of this chapter, it is measurements of the brightness and the spectrum of a distant galaxy that can lead to determinations of its distance and speed, respectively. We start by examining just what 'light' is.

3.1 Let there be light!

Our eyes are sensitive to light that comprises the familiar rainbow of colours, but these colours are merely a tiny part of the vast **electromagnetic spectrum**. One way to describe the different components of the electromagnetic spectrum is in terms of waves.

A **wave** may be defined as a *periodic*, or regularly repeating, disturbance that transports *energy* from one place to another. For instance, a stone dropped into the centre of a pond generates waves on the water surface, which travel outwards and eventually cause a cork at the edge of the pond to bob up and down with a regular motion. Similarly, a sudden motion of part of the Earth's crust generates seismic waves that travel through the Earth, and may cause damage to buildings some distance away on the surface. Another image that the word 'wave' often conjures up is that of water waves on the sea.

If you've ever been on a beach you will have seen or heard waves break onto the shore with a fairly regular time interval between each 'crash' and the next. Each crash represents one wave crest breaking onto the shore, and the time interval between two of them is known as the period of the wave. In general, the period of a wave may be defined as the time between one part of the wave profile (say the crest) passing a fixed point in space and the *next* identical part of the wave profile (the next crest) passing the same fixed point. In the example here, the fixed point is the shoreline.

As well as being periodic with time, a wave is also periodic as far as its spatial extent is concerned. The word wave is often used to describe a *single* crash onto the beach, but it really refers to the entire sequence of crests and troughs, stretching away into the distance. The distance between one wave crest and the next is known as the **wavelength** of the wave. In general, the wavelength of a wave is defined as the distance between one part of the wave profile, at a particular instant in time, and the *next* identical part of the wave profile at the same instant of time. Two adjacent crests of the wave are a convenient pair of locations to use for this definition, although any pair of similar points will do.

You can think of electromagnetic waves as similar to waves on the ocean. In the case of ocean waves, the wave motion takes place on the surface of the water, whereas in the case of electromagnetic waves the wave motion takes the form of varying electric and magnetic disturbances. The exact nature of these electromagnetic waves is not important for our discussion, and if you keep in mind a visual image of water waves, that will be fine.

The key thing is that each colour of light corresponds to electromagnetic waves of a different wavelength. Visible light spans the range of wavelengths from about 400 billionths of a metre (400 nanometres or 400×10^{-9} m) to 700 billionths of a metre (700 nanometres or 700×10^{-9} m). Violet light has the shortest wavelength and red the longest (Figure 9). However, at even longer wavelengths are found first infrared radiation, then microwaves and radio waves, whilst at wavelengths shorter than the visible are found ultraviolet radiation, then X-rays and gamma-rays. The full electromagnetic spectrum is shown in Figure 10.

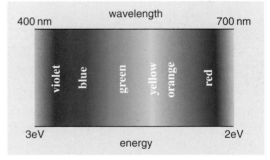

Figure 9 Different colours of light correspond to radiation of different wavelengths.

Although electromagnetic radiation travels from place to place like a wave, it is emitted or absorbed by matter as if it is composed of a stream of particles, called **photons**. There is no conflict between these two approaches, it's just that one picture (waves) is useful for describing the way electromagnetic radiation propagates and another picture (particles) is useful for describing the way it interacts with matter. This is double description is referred to as **wave–particle duality.**

Like any particles, photons can be characterized by how much energy they carry. The unit of energy used to quantify a photon's energy is the electronvolt, which you met earlier. Again, it's not too important just what this unit of energy is, but conveniently

Figure 10 The electromagnetic spectrum.

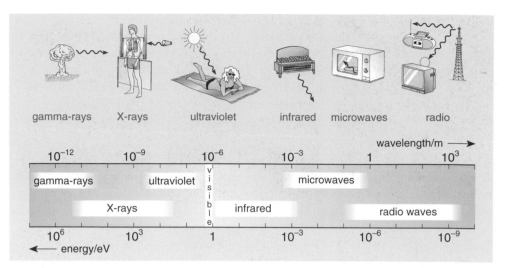

photons of red light each have an energy of about 2 eV, and photons of violet light each have an energy of about 3 eV. At lower energies than red light are the infrared, microwave and radio wave parts of the electromagnetic spectrum, and at higher energies are the ultraviolet, X-ray and gamma-ray regions. As you can see on Figure 10, X-ray or gamma-ray photons have energies of many kiloelectronvolts (thousands of electronvolts) or many megaelectronvolts (millions of electronvolts).

A photon is also known as a *quantum* of electromagnetic radiation. Photons therefore lie at the heart of the the theory of **quantum physics,** which originated in the early years of the 20th century with the work of people such as Max Planck, Niels Bohr, Erwin Schrödinger, Werner Heisenberg, Wolfgang Pauli and Louis de Broglie (Figure 11). A key result of the theory is that atoms can exist only with particular values of energy, known as **energy levels**. When an atom has a particular energy it is said to be in a particular **quantum state**. The values of the energy of each of these quantum states are specific to each different type of atom: hydrogen, carbon, oxygen, iron, etc. Furthermore, when atoms make transitions between different quantum states, such that the atoms *lose* energy, then photons are *emitted*. Alternatively, when atoms *absorb* photons, they again make transitions between different quantum states, but this time such that the atoms *gain* energy. These two processes are illustrated in Figure 12. In the simplest atom, hydrogen, the energy levels are each separated by energies of only a few electronvolts.

Each photon that is emitted by an atom as it makes a transition between energy levels carries a certain amount of energy, the magnitude of which depends on the difference in energy between two energy levels of the atom concerned. Therefore,

> energy of emitted photon *equals* energy of upper level *minus* energy of lower level (1a)

Since the atom is allowed to exist only in certain quantum states, each with a specific energy level, only photons with particular energies are emitted. The distribution of the photons according to their energy, shown for example in Figure 13a, is known as an **emission spectrum** of the atoms involved. The bright, coloured lines at the top of the figure indicate the presence of photons with particular energies; and each of these energies corresponds to the difference in energy between two certain allowed states of the atoms. Dark regions indicate that no photons with these energies are emitted — there are no pairs of atomic energy levels separated by these particular energy values.

(a)

(b)

(c)

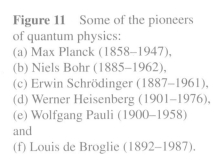

Figure 11   Some of the pioneers of quantum physics:
(a) Max Planck (1858–1947),
(b) Niels Bohr (1885–1962),
(c) Erwin Schrödinger (1887–1961),
(d) Werner Heisenberg (1901–1976),
(e) Wolfgang Pauli (1900–1958)
and
(f) Louis de Broglie (1892–1987).

(d)

(e)

(f)

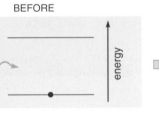
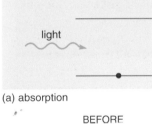

(a) absorption

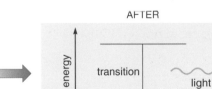
(b) emission

Figure 12   The two horizontal lines in each part of this figure represent two of the possible energies of the atom — two of the possible energy levels. When the atom occupies an energy level, the energy level is marked with a dot. (The width of the horizontal lines in this diagram is of no significance.) You can think of these energy levels as something like the shelves on a bookcase. A book may sit on any of the shelves, and when it is on a higher shelf it has a greater energy than when it is on a lower shelf. (a) When a photon is absorbed by an atom, the atom makes a transition from a lower energy level to a higher energy level. (b) A photon is emitted by an atom when the atom makes a transition from a higher energy level to a lower energy level.

Conversely, if photons with a range of energies are directed at particular atoms, only photons with certain energies are absorbed. As before,

energy of absorbed photon *equals* energy of upper level *minus* energy of lower level

(1b)

The remaining (unabsorbed) photons that emerge are distributed according to their energy as shown in Figure 13b, and this is known as an **absorption spectrum** of the atoms involved. The dark lines at the top of the diagram indicate that photons with particular energies have been absorbed, and these energies correspond to differences between allowed energy levels of the atoms involved. Bright regions indicate that no photons with these energies are absorbed — there are no atomic energy levels separated by these particular energy values.

Often, you will see line spectra represented pictorially as in the upper panels of Figure 13. However, to illustrate things more quantitatively, we plot the spectrum as a graph. The equivalent graphs of these spectra are shown in the lower panels of Figure 13.

After this discussion of the line spectra of atoms, you may be wondering how it is possible to get a continuous spectrum, such as that shown earlier in Figure 9. Continuous spectra contain a continuous distribution of photon energies. They can be produced by heating the tungsten filament of an electric light bulb to a very high temperature, or from an electric fire, for instance. The red glow from the fire is not attributable to any particular photon energy; this spectrum is continuous, like that of the light bulb, except that the brightest part of the fire's visible spectrum is the red part.

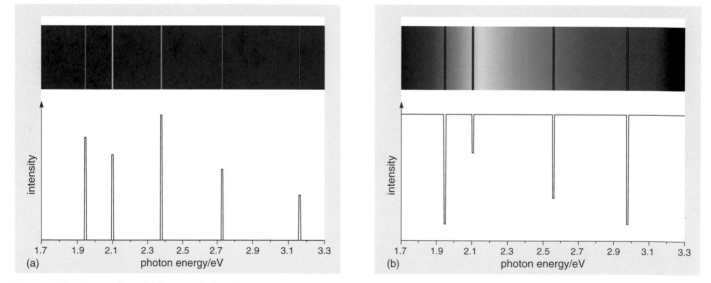

Figure 13 Examples of (a) an emission line spectrum and (b) an absorption line spectrum. The upper panels show pictorial representations of spectra in the energy range corresponding to visible light. The lower panels show these same spectra, but converted into graphs of intensity against energy, known as spectral distributions. You can think of the spectral distributions as representing how dark or bright the spectra appear at a given energy: the brighter the spectrum, the more intense the light registered in the spectral distribution, at a given energy. The two ways of representing a particular emission spectrum or absorption spectrum are entirely equivalent to each other. However, the spectral distributions are more quantitative, since they show not only where the emission lines and absorption lines occur, but also how intense the light is in each part of the spectrum.

The continuity of the spectrum from a heated object results from the fact that we are not studying emission from individual atoms, but the effect of many atoms together in a solid. In a solid metal, like tungsten, the atoms are arranged in a regular fashion, and some of the electrons are shared by the whole array of atoms. This is what makes the conduction of electricity possible. Though highly mobile, these electrons are confined, or bound, within the metal. They are associated with energy levels, but there are so many levels, and their energies are so close together, that they form a continuous energy band that is typically a few electronvolts wide. Transitions within this band give rise to a continuous range of photon energies, and hence a continuous spectrum.

Continuous spectra can also be represented as graphs, and two examples are shown in Figure 14. These are the spectral distributions that would be produced by a hot metal object at the temperatures shown. Since the peak intensities of these spectra occur at energies of less than 2 eV, these heated metals emit most of their radiation in the infrared part of the spectrum. However, there is also some emission in the region between 2 eV and 3 eV — the visible part of the spectrum. This is why a conventional light bulb (whose tungsten filament reaches a temperature of about 2500 °C) produces (some) light. Notice though that most of the radiation produced by a conventional light bulb is 'wasted' because it emerges in the infrared part of the spectrum.

In fact, many objects have continuous spectra whose distributions have similar shapes to those in Figure 14. These spectral distributions depend *only* on the temperature of the object, not its composition. The important point to note about such spectra is that at higher temperatures, the peak intensity occurs at higher energies. We shall return to such spectra again in Chapter 4.

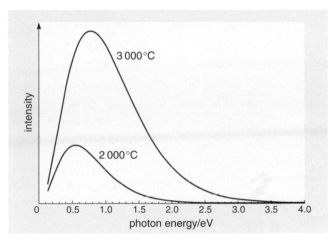

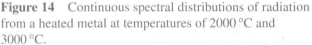

Figure 14 Continuous spectral distributions of radiation from a heated metal at temperatures of 2000 °C and 3000 °C.

3.2 The distance to galaxies

Astronomical distances are so enormous that metres (or even kilometres) are too small a unit with which to measure them. For this reason, cosmologists usually use a different unit known as the **parsec** (symbol: pc), which is equal to about 30 thousand billion kilometres (3×10^{13} km). In terms of another unit you may have heard of, a parsec is equal to about 3 **light years** (symbol: ly). In other words, it would take a beam of light about three years to travel a distance of one parsec. We may write

$$1 \, \text{pc} \sim 3 \, \text{ly} \sim 3 \times 10^{13} \, \text{km}$$

where the symbol '~' may be read as 'is approximately equal to'.

To give you an idea of the sort of distance scales that are involved in the Universe, the distance from the Earth to the Sun is about 1.5×10^8 km or only 0.000 005 pc, and the Solar System out to the orbit of Pluto has a diameter of about 1.5×10^{10} km or 0.0005 pc. The nearest star to the Sun, Proxima Centauri, is about 1.3 pc (or about 4 ly) away. As illustrated in Figure 15, our own galaxy, the Milky Way, is about 40 000 pc, or 40 kpc (40 kiloparsecs), in diameter and one of our nearest neighbours, the Andromeda Galaxy, is about 660 000 pc or 660 kpc (660 kiloparsecs) distant from

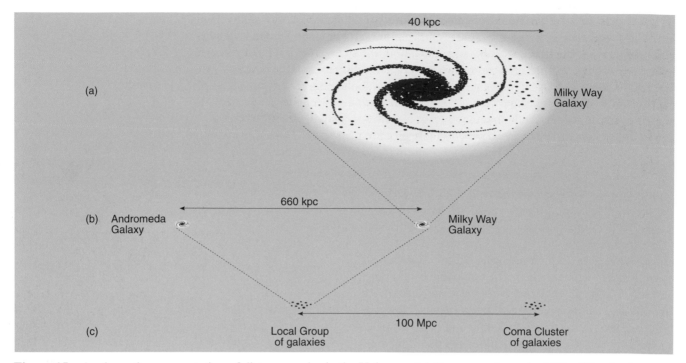

Figure 15   A schematic representation of distance scales in the Universe. (a) Our own galaxy, the Milky Way, is about 40 kpc in diameter. (b) The distance from our own galaxy to the Andromeda Galaxy is about 660 kpc, which is around 16 times the diameter of the Milky Way. (c) Our own galaxy and the Andromeda Galaxy are both part of the so-called Local Group of galaxies. The distance from the Local Group to the Coma Cluster of galaxies is about 100 Mpc, which means that the Coma Cluster is around 150 times farther away from us than is the Andromeda Galaxy.

us. Clusters of galaxies typically lie at distances of several hundred million parsecs away (one million parsecs is written as 1 Mpc or 1 megaparsec), or even several billion parsec away (one billion parsecs is written as 1 Gpc or 1 gigaparsec).

⬤ What is a distance of 1 Gpc expressed in metres?

◯ Since 1 pc $= 3 \times 10^{13}$ km, so 1 Gpc $= 10^9 \times 3 \times 10^{13}$ km $= 3 \times 10^{22}$ km. Converting into metres, 1 Gpc $= 3 \times 10^{22} \times 10^3$ m $= 3 \times 10^{25}$ m.

Measuring the distance to galaxies is a difficult business. Obviously one cannot simply 'take a journey' to the galaxy in question and measure the distance that way. As noted earlier, all that we have to go on is the *light* from the galaxy and, in particular, how *bright* the galaxy appears to be. However, in certain circumstances this turns out to be enough information to work out the distance to a galaxy. The reason is that the **brightness** of a galaxy depends on two things: the amount of light it emits (this is called the **luminosity** of the galaxy), and also how far away it is. To appreciate this, consider the following 'thought experiment'.

⬤ Imagine that you have two identical torches — both have the same luminosity and so they emit the same power. You switch them on, then place one of them 100 m away from you, and the other only 20 m away. In the dark, how can you tell which of the two torches is nearer to you?

◯ The nearer torch will appear to be brighter than the one that is more distant. So, even though the two torches have the same luminosity, they have different brightnesses because they are at different distances away from you.

To appreciate the relationship between the luminosity and the brightness of an object, look at the situation depicted in Figure 16. This shows two galaxies labelled A and B, which have the same luminosity, but are at different distances from the Earth. As the light from each galaxy travels out into space, so the light spreads out over the surfaces of imaginary spheres, centred on the galaxy. By the time it reaches the Earth, the light from the more distant galaxy is spread out over a larger sphere than the light from the nearer galaxy. So the more distant galaxy will appear less bright than the nearby galaxy because its light is spread out over a bigger area.

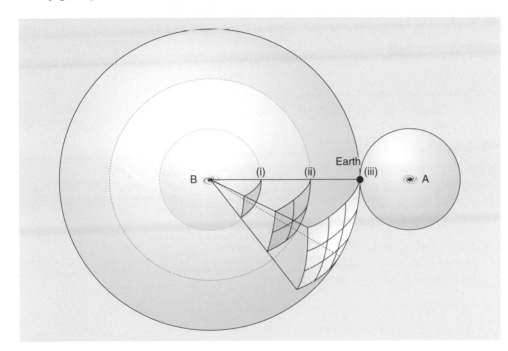

Figure 16 The light from distant galaxies spreads out over the surfaces of imaginary spheres centred on each galaxy. Galaxies A and B have the same luminosity but are situated at different distances from the Earth. For galaxy B, three spherical surfaces are shown at regularly increasing distances away from the galaxy. Galaxy A is closer than galaxy B, its light is spread out over a smaller sphere by the time it reaches the Earth, and so it appears brighter.

In fact, the brightness of a galaxy is *defined* to be equal to its luminosity divided by the surface area of an imaginary sphere whose radius is equal to the distance from the Earth to the galaxy. How does the surface area of a sphere depend upon its radius? Quite simply, if the radius doubles, the surface area increases by a factor of four; if the radius increases by a factor of three, the surface area increases by a factor of nine. In other words, the surface area of a sphere is **proportional to** its radius squared. So in turn we can say that the brightness of a galaxy is proportional to its luminosity divided by the square of its distance away.

$$\text{brightness is proportional to } \frac{\text{luminosity}}{\text{distance squared}} \qquad (2)$$

This relationship between brightness and luminosity is said to be an **inverse square law**. Any relationship where one quantity *decreases* as the square of another quantity *increases* can be classified in this way. You will meet two other examples of inverse square laws later in the book.

As we have repeatedly emphasized, when observing a distant galaxy, cosmologists can measure its brightness, but if the luminosity of the galaxy is known, then the distance to it can be calculated. But how do we determine the luminosity of the galaxy in the first place? One such method is as follows.

Figure 17 An image of the Coma Cluster of galaxies, covering an area of sky about one-quarter the size of the full Moon. This cluster of galaxies is situated at about 100 Mpc away, and individual members have a range of different brightnesses. In fact, virtually all of the objects in this image are galaxies in the cluster. An exception is the bright object at the top, centre which is a foreground star within our own galaxy. (The 'spikes' are an artefact caused by the camera.)

Clusters of galaxies can contain anything from a few dozen to a few thousand individual galaxies. When cosmologists look at a cluster, such as the Coma Cluster of galaxies shown in Figure 17, they see that all the galaxies within it have different brightnesses. Now, on the scale of the Universe it is usually adequate to assume that all galaxies in a single cluster are at about the same distance from us. (The distances between individual galaxies in a cluster — a few hundred kiloparsecs — are small when compared with the distance of the cluster from us — usually hundreds of megaparsecs.) So the variation in brightness of galaxies *within* a cluster must reflect an *intrinsic* variation in luminosity from one member galaxy to the next. The assumption that cosmologists make is that, wherever they find reasonably large clusters (say more than a hundred members), the *tenth brightest* galaxy in any one cluster has roughly the same luminosity as the tenth brightest galaxy in any other cluster. The tenth brightest is therefore assumed to be a typical galaxy for any cluster and is referred to as a **standard candle**. Although details vary depending on the region of the spectrum in which the luminosity is measured, a typical value for the luminosity of the tenth brightest galaxy in a cluster is around 10^{41} watts. (For comparison recall that a typical household lightbulb has a luminosity of only 10^2 watts!)

In practice, the procedure for determining the distance to a cluster is often based on *comparing* the brightnesses of a pair of galaxies in different clusters, which are assumed to have the same luminosity (both are tenth brightest), and where the distance to one of them is already known.

⬤ Suppose that Figure 16 shows the tenth brightest galaxies, labelled A and B, in a couple of clusters. Galaxy B is three times farther away than galaxy A. How will their brightnesses compare?

◯ Galaxy B will appear to be $3 \times 3 = 9$ times fainter than galaxy A.

⬤ If, instead, galaxy A were 36 times brighter than galaxy B, and situated 100 Mpc away, what would be the distance to the cluster in which galaxy B sits?

◯ Galaxy A and galaxy B are both tenth brightest in their clusters so we assume that both have the same luminosity. Since galaxy B is 36× fainter than galaxy A, its light must be spread out over the surface of a sphere which has 36× greater area than that for galaxy A. The surface area of a sphere is proportional to its radius squared, so to get a surface area that is 36× larger, the radius of the sphere must be 6× greater (since 6 squared = 36). So galaxy B must be six times farther away than galaxy A, i.e. at a distance of 600 Mpc.

Measurements of nearby clusters of galaxies, whose distances can be estimated by more direct methods, indicate that the assumption of the tenth brightest galaxies all having roughly the same luminosity is valid. Therefore, we can assume that the luminosity of the tenth brightest galaxy in *any* cluster is the same, and so the distance to *any* cluster can be found by measuring the brightness of its tenth brightest member.

3.3 The speed of galaxies

We now consider how to measure the speed with which a galaxy is moving away from (or towards) us. Once again, this technique is based on measurements made on the light emitted by a galaxy, but this time we need to examine the spectrum of light — how it is distributed with wavelength — rather than the total amount of light emitted. It may not be immediately obvious what spectra have to do with speed measurements, but this will soon become apparent.

The way to measure the spectrum of light from a star or galaxy is to point a telescope at the object in question and allow the light to pass through something called a **diffraction grating**. This is a device that separates the light according to its wavelength. You can often see a similar effect if you reflect light from the surface of a compact disc or view a bright light source through a fine net curtain. The tracks on the CD or the threads in the net curtain take the form of a series of regularly spaced fine lines that diffract the light and separate the colours into a spectrum. In a telescope, the spectrum is recorded using an electronic imaging device, similar to that in a home video camera, and the information is stored on a computer for processing.

When the light from stars or galaxies is spread out to form a spectrum (Figure 18a), the spectra are seen to contain many dark lines superimposed on the overall bright background. These are **absorption lines** and are due to the presence of particular types of atom. As noted earlier, each type of atom absorbs light of particular wavelengths. The bright, continuous, background in the spectrum from a star is produced by photons coming from deep in its atmosphere. As these photons emerge through the star's cooler, outermost layers, photons with specific energies are absorbed by atoms. The absorption lines are therefore characteristic of the particular elements that are present in the outermost layers of the star.

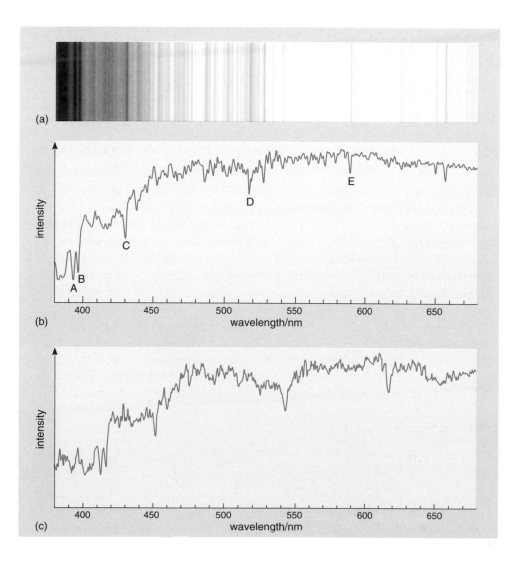

Figure 18 (a) and (b) show two representations of the spectrum of a star within our own Galaxy. Here, violet light is displayed towards the left of the spectrum (wavelength 380 nm) and red light to the right (wavelength 680 nm). (a) An image of the spectrum. (b) The spectral distribution of the same spectrum. Absorption lines are visible as dark bands in (a) and as dips in the graph in (b). (c) A spectrum of a distant galaxy shown in the same representation as (b).

As already explained, there are two ways of representing such a spectrum. First, a spectrum can be displayed as an image. Figure 18a shows such an image of a spectrum from a typical star. The intensity of the light at any point in the spectrum is represented by the grey scale of the image at that point — darker grey indicates lower intensity. Second, the spectrum may be displayed as a graph, known as a spectral distribution, as shown in Figure 18b. This is the same spectrum as in Figure 18a, just displayed in the alternative representation.

When the spectra of distant galaxies are examined, similar absorption line spectra are seen to those of stars in our own galaxy. An example of a galaxy spectrum is shown in Figure 18c, where it may be compared with the spectrum of the typical star (within our own Galaxy) in Figure 18b. It is not surprising that the two spectra are rather similar, since the spectrum of the galaxy is simply the sum of the spectra of the billions of stars that comprise it. Because most galaxies are far away, telescopes are unable to distinguish individual stars within them.

○ Five of the strongest absorption lines in the spectrum of the star are labelled A–E in Figure 18b. Can you identify this same pattern of lines in the spectrum of the galaxy (Figure 18c)? What do you notice about the positions of the lines in the galaxy spectrum, relative to their positions in the star spectrum?

○ The same basic *pattern* of absorption lines appears in each spectrum, but the *positions* of the lines are different. In particular, the lines in the spectrum of the galaxy (Figure 18c) are displaced to longer wavelengths, relative to those in the star (Figure 18b). For example, absorption line C appears at about 430 nanometres (nm) in Figure 18b but at about 450 nm in Figure 18c.

It is assumed that the absorption lines seen in the spectrum of the distant galaxy are due to the *same* elements as those seen in the spectra of the Sun and other stars within our own galaxy. The difference is that the absorption lines in the spectrum of the distant galaxy are shifted towards longer wavelengths.

Shifted wavelengths have a very natural interpretation in everyday life. The phenomenon is known as the **Doppler effect** and it is probably familiar to you in the context of sound waves, although it applies equally to any wave motion, including electromagnetic radiation such as light. The Doppler effect with sound is perhaps most noticeable when an approaching ambulance sounds its siren or as a speeding car races past. As the vehicle approaches and then recedes, apart from growing louder and then fainter, the pitch of the sound is perceived as higher when the vehicle is approaching than when it is receding. As shown in Figure 19, this can be understood in terms of the sound waves getting 'bunched up' in front of the vehicle as it approaches, and 'stretched out' behind the vehicle as it recedes. This happens simply because the vehicle moves between the time it emits a particular crest of the sound wave and when it emits the next crest. The bunching up in front of the vehicle causes the wavelength of the sound reaching your ears to be shorter than if the vehicle were stationary, and the stretching out behind the vehicle causes the wavelength to be longer.

A shorter wavelength of sound implies a higher pitch of the sound. So, as the vehicle approaches, you hear a higher pitch than if the vehicle were stationary. Conversely, as it recedes from you, the pitch will be lower than if the vehicle were stationary. A similar effect is observed with light.

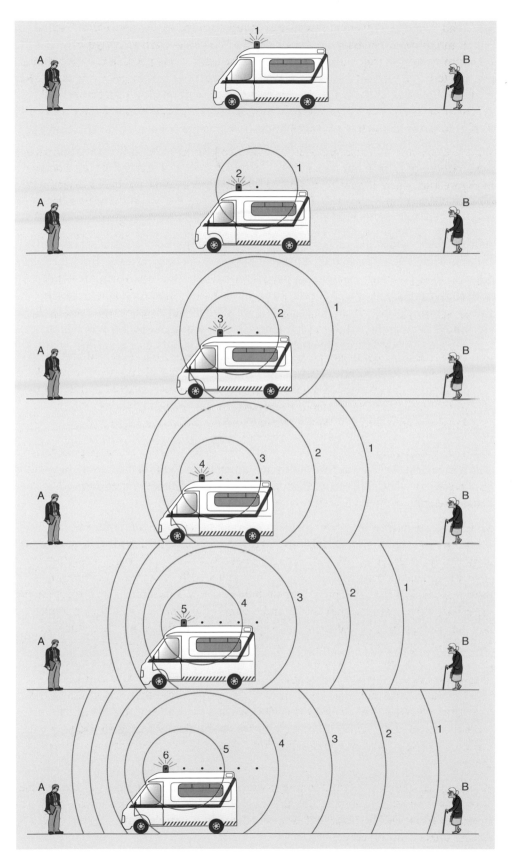

Figure 19 A demonstration of the Doppler effect with sound (not to scale). The ambulance sounds its siren as it moves towards observer A. Six successive time intervals are shown in the six sketches, with the curved lines representing successive crests of the sound wave emitted by the siren. You may like to think of the curved lines as being similar to the ripples produced when a stone is dropped into a pond — the wave crests spread out from the centre just as shown here. The wavelength is then just the distance between any two successive crests at any point. By the time the second wave crest is emitted, the ambulance has caught up slightly with the first wave crest. By the time the third wave crest is emitted, the ambulance has caught up with the second wave crest, and so on. The consequence is that a person at A will perceive a sound wave with a shorter wavelength than that emitted by the siren when at rest, whilst a person at B will perceive a longer wavelength.

○ The wavelength of sound waves may be appreciated by the pitch of the sound perceived by the human ear. How does the wavelength of light manifest itself to human senses?

○ The wavelength of a light wave is perceived by the human eye as the colour of the light.

A shift in the colour to longer wavelengths (towards the red end of the spectrum) is an indication of motion away from the observer, a shift in the colour to shorter wavelengths (towards the blue) is an indication of motion towards the observer.

○ Which way is the spectrum shifted in Figure 18c?

○ It is shifted towards longer wavelengths, i.e. towards the red.

Astronomers say that the galaxy spectrum shown in Figure 18c displays a **redshift**, and this is interpreted as an indication that the galaxy is moving away from the Earth. Spectral lines produced by atoms in the galaxy have the same wavelength as lines produced in similar atomic processes in an Earth-based laboratory. But since the galaxy is moving away from the Earth, the wavelengths of its lines observed on Earth are shifted towards the red. By exactly the same reasoning, a spectrum in which features are shifted towards the blue, known not surprisingly as a blueshift, would indicate that the galaxy is moving towards the Earth.

The numerical value of the redshift, or blueshift, is defined as the *change* in wavelength divided by the *original* wavelength:

redshift = change in wavelength/original wavelength   (3a)

Alternatively, we can turn this definition around and say that the *change* in wavelength is equal to the redshift, or blueshift, multiplied by the *original* wavelength:

change in wavelength = redshift × original wavelength   (3b)

The original wavelength is assumed to be that which would be produced by the same types of atom in a laboratory on Earth. It is also sometimes known as the *rest wavelength*, since it is the wavelength that would be observed from a stationary source. To identify which types of atom produced the absorption lines in a galaxy spectrum, a certain amount of pattern matching is required to compare a series of lines rather than just one or two individual lines. The same value of the redshift must apply to *all* lines in a spectrum of a certain galaxy, whatever their individual wavelengths.

For the speeds that we shall be considering here, the speed of motion of the galaxy is equal to the redshift (or blueshift) multiplied by the speed of light:

speed of galaxy = redshift × speed of light   (4a)

Alternatively, the redshift (or blueshift) is equal to the speed of motion of the galaxy divided by the speed of light:

redshift = speed of galaxy/speed of light   (4b)

The speed of light is about 300 000 kilometres per second, which we can write concisely as 3×10^5 km s^{-1}. Notice the use of 's^{-1}' to indicate 'per second' — this is a common practice that you will often see in scientific writing.

So, if the wavelength of an absorption line in the spectrum of a galaxy is measured and compared with the wavelength of the same spectral line, as measured in a laboratory, the redshift, or blueshift, of the galaxy can be calculated. This can then be converted into a **recession speed** (motion away) or an approach speed (motion towards).

Worked example 1

As an illustration of the use of the shifts of spectral lines to determine speeds, what is the recession speed of the galaxy whose spectrum is shown in Figure 18c? The spectral lines in the spectrum of the star (Figure 18b) occur at the *same* wavelengths as in spectra produced in the laboratory. It may therefore be assumed that the star is 'at rest' with respect to the Earth.

Answer

The absorption line labelled C in the spectrum of the star occurs at a wavelength of 431 nm. The corresponding line in the spectrum of the galaxy (Figure 18c) occurs at a wavelength of 452 nm. The rest wavelength is therefore 431 nm, and the change in wavelength of this line when observed in the galaxy spectrum is (452 − 431) nm = 21 nm. Since the observed wavelength is longer than the rest wavelength, we are dealing with a redshift here and the galaxy must be receding from us. The redshift is calculated as 21 nm/431 nm = 0.049.

The speed that this redshift corresponds to is then simply $(0.049 \times 3 \times 10^5)$ km s^{-1} or about 15 000 km s^{-1}. (Note that the star that produced the spectrum in Figure 18a and b may actually be moving too. However, speeds of up to 70 km s^{-1} would produce wavelength shifts of less than 0.1 nm, and so would be negligible on the scale of Figure 18. So although the star may actually be moving quite fast by everyday standards we can treat it as being at rest in this case.) ◄

As noted earlier, our galaxy, the Milky Way, is one member of a small family of nearby galaxies known as the Local Group. Within the Local Group, a variety of redshifts and blueshifts are observed. This indicates that, in our local neighbourhood, the galaxies are milling around in a fairly random manner. However, if galaxies and clusters of galaxies that are more distant than the Local Group are observed, a remarkable effect is seen: *all* the galaxies exhibit redshifts, *none* exhibit blueshifts.

⬤ Why is this remarkable?

⬤ This is remarkable because it shows that *all* clusters of galaxies in the Universe are receding from our own Local Group of galaxies!

3.4 The Hubble relationship

You have seen that the recession speeds of distant galaxies can be determined by using redshift measurements, and that their distances may be calculated by comparing the brightnesses of galaxies with their luminosities. When these results are examined for a large number of clusters of galaxies, a quite startling relationship becomes apparent:

The farther away a galaxy is, the faster it is moving.

Figure 20   Edwin Powell Hubble (1889–1953) was an American astronomer who was the first to provide definite proof that the objects we now know as galaxies lie far beyond the Milky Way. He established the speed–distance relationship for distant galaxies, and the constant relating the two is known as the Hubble constant. He also produced a classification scheme for galaxies — dividing them into ellipticals, spirals and barred spirals — based on their shape. He worked for most of his career at the Mount Wilson Observatory in California. The Hubble Space Telescope, launched by NASA in 1990, is named in his honour.

The first person to point this out was the American astronomer Edwin Hubble (Figure 20) in 1929. The Hubble relationship may be expressed by the simple statement:

> The recession speed of a galaxy is equal to a certain number, known as the **Hubble constant**, multiplied by its distance away:
>
> speed of galaxy = Hubble constant × distance to galaxy   (5a)
>
> or equivalently, the distance to a galaxy is equal to its recession speed divided by a certain number, known as the Hubble constant:
>
> distance to galaxy = speed of galaxy/Hubble constant   (5b)
>
> Alternatively, we may define the Hubble constant itself as equal to the recession speed of a galaxy divided by its distance away.
>
> Hubble constant = speed of galaxy/distance to galaxy   (5c)

○ Since the recession speed of a galaxy is typically measured in the unit km s^{-1}, and the distance to a galaxy is usually measured in the unit Mpc, what would be a sensible unit for the Hubble constant?

○ The Hubble constant is equal to speed divided by distance, so in this case the unit is $\dfrac{\text{km s}^{-1}}{\text{Mpc}}$. A sensible unit for the Hubble constant is therefore km s^{-1} Mpc^{-1} (i.e. kilometres per second per megaparsec), and this is in fact what is usually used.

Activity 1   The virtual telescope

In order for you to consolidate your understanding of the measurements that lead to the Hubble relationship, you should now work through this computer activity and derive your own value for the Hubble constant.

This computer activity takes the form of a virtual experiment. You will have control of a powerful telescope with which you can measure the redshifts and brightnesses of galaxies within several clusters. By converting the redshifts into speeds of recession and determining distances from the brightness measurements, you will be able to determine a value for the Hubble constant. As you will see later, the Hubble constant also gives a measure of the age of the Universe.

In case you think that sitting in front of a computer is no substitute for visiting a real observatory, you might be surprised to learn that, even at a real observatory, professional astronomers usually spend the whole night sitting in front of a computer too. Sometimes, the astronomer is not even present at the observatory, but controls the telescope remotely over the Internet. Thanks to the advent of electronic imaging devices, the days (or nights!) of peering through a telescope eyepiece are long gone at all of the big observatories.

In fact, the telescope you'll be using has many advantages over the real thing. First, you don't have to travel halfway round the world in order to use it. You're not gasping for breath at an altitude of over 4000 m, and you don't have to stay awake all night. The telescope has an imager, a photometer (for measuring brightnesses) and a spectrometer (for obtaining spectra), each available at the click of a mouse button, and is available for use whenever you want it. In the real world, an application to use a telescope would be made a year in advance, and be subject to competition from hundreds of other astronomers. Only the very best observing proposals get awarded a few nights at the telescope, and even then the weather may be too bad to do anything. This telescope has perpetually cloud-free skies, and what's more you can see both the Northern and Southern hemisphere skies from the same observatory. In many ways this is a big improvement over a real telescope!

In your use of the virtual telescope, just as at a real observatory, you will be guided in the use of the telescope by a 'support astronomer'. At real observatories, the support astronomer is a staff member of the observatory who is familiar with the operation of all the equipment and is always on hand to help visiting astronomers carry out their programme of observations. The virtual telescope's support astronomer knows exactly how that telescope operates and although she will give you all the information you need to operate it, we summarize the key features of the package here for reference.

- The package opens with an image of the night sky, on which eight clusters of galaxies are highlighted. The clusters have been chosen to be representative and at a range of redshift (hence distance).

- When you select an individual cluster, the virtual telescope provides an image of the cluster. You then have the choice of selecting either the spectrometer or photometer to carry the investigation further. The **spectrometer** measures the spectrum of a single galaxy selected from the image, whilst the **photometer** measures the brightnesses of all galaxies within the image.

- If you select the spectrometer you will then be asked to choose an individual galaxy within the cluster and will obtain a spectrum of the galaxy in question over the wavelength range between about 350 nm and 650 nm.

- On calling up a 'reference spectrum', you will be invited to identify common features in the two spectra, from which a redshift is calculated. This redshift is converted into a recession speed that can be saved in a table of results for each cluster.

- The procedure may be repeated for other features in the same spectrum and for spectra of other galaxies in the same cluster — all of which should give similar results for the recession speed of the cluster in question. All the results for each cluster are collected together and averaged.

- When you return to the imager screen and select the photometer option, the virtual telescope measures the brightnesses of (up to) 20 galaxies in the cluster. You then select the tenth brightest galaxy in the cluster from the information presented. (You may sort the list into brightness order to help with this.)

- By comparing the brightness of this galaxy with that of a standard tenth brightest galaxy with a known luminosity, the distance to the cluster in question is calculated in metres and megaparsecs. The distance may also be saved to the results page for the cluster.

- The whole procedure of speed and distance measurement is repeated for up to eight clusters of galaxies. Each cluster has its own page of results.

- When results have been obtained for several clusters of galaxies, the average recession speed and distance for each cluster may be plotted on a graph, from which the Hubble constant is measured.

All the measurements, calculations and graph plotting are performed automatically by the virtual telescope, according to your instructions. You should note though that the virtual telescope screen display uses symbols to represent speeds, distances, redshifts, wavelengths, etc. If this use of symbols to represent numbers is unfamiliar to you, please don't worry about it. You will still be able to work through the activity quite successfully by following the instructions of the support astronomer. Another feature is that numbers are displayed by the virtual telescope in a similar format to that used by calculators. So a number like 1.00×10^{41} will be displayed as 1.00E41, for instance.

Start up the virtual telescope computer software package now, and follow the instructions of the support astronomer.

'The virtual telescope' only allowed you to make measurements of a maximum of eight clusters of galaxies. Despite this, you should have come up with a value for the Hubble constant that is similar to the most accurate determinations made today. Figure 21 shows a graph of the recession speed and distance for several hundred clusters of galaxies. As with your own measurements, a straight line has been drawn through the data points. The slope of this line tells us the *rate* at which recession speed increases with distance. A steeper slope means that recession speeds increase rapidly as we observe ever more distant galaxies; a shallower slope implies that recession speeds increase only gradually for distant galaxies. The actual value of the slope of this line can be measured as the overall increase in speed ($3.6 \times 10^4\,\mathrm{km\,s^{-1}}$) divided by the overall increase in distance (500 Mpc). It gives the value of the Hubble constant as $72\,\mathrm{km\,s^{-1}\,Mpc^{-1}}$.

Figure 21 The Hubble relationship between the recession speed of a galaxy and its distance from us, illustrated with a sample of several hundred clusters of galaxies. Note the redshift scale on the right of the graph. The large scatter that is apparent in these points reflects the difficulty in accurately determining the recession speed and distance of these clusters. The redshifts (and hence speeds) are typically measured to an accuracy of 10%, whereas the distances are only accurate to about a factor of two in some cases.

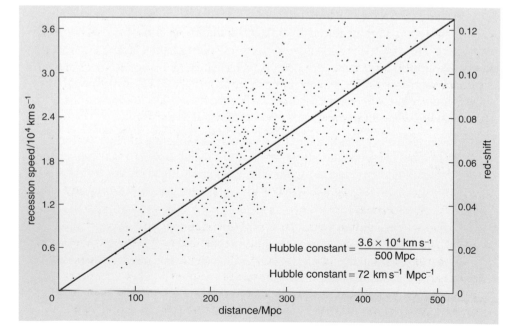

What does the value for the Hubble constant imply? Well, look at its unit: kilometres per second per megaparsec. This means that for every megaparsec of distance out into the Universe, the galaxies and clusters appear to be moving about $72 \, \text{km} \, \text{s}^{-1}$ faster.

We have only discussed one method for finding the distances to galaxies. In practice other techniques are also used, each appropriate to a range of distances, with one building on the results of another. Because each of these measurements is subject to uncertainty of one sort or another — either in the measurements themselves or the theoretical basis for them — the answers that different people obtain for the Hubble constant do vary significantly. As of the end of 2002, the most reliable measurement obtained from observations with the Hubble Space Telescope puts the value at $72 \, \text{km} \, \text{s}^{-1} \, \text{Mpc}^{-1}$ with an uncertainty of 10% (i.e the value probably lies between about $65 \, \text{km} \, \text{s}^{-1} \, \text{Mpc}^{-1}$ and $80 \, \text{km} \, \text{s}^{-1} \, \text{Mpc}^{-1}$). By the time you read this, it is possible that a more precise value for the Hubble constant will have been obtained using one of the new generation of powerful telescopes.

3.5 Expanding space

You've seen how cosmologists obtain the observational data on which the Hubble relationship is based. We now turn to a consideration of how it may be interpreted, and then look at the consequences of this interpretation for the properties of the Universe in the distant past.

Wherever cosmologists look they see galaxies rushing away from the Local Group, and the farther away the galaxies are, the faster they appear to move. The interpretation of this is that space *itself* is expanding uniformly, and the same behaviour would be observed *wherever* in the Universe one happened to be. Now, it's quite difficult to appreciate this for our three-dimensional Universe, so, in order to make things simpler, let's consider a one-dimensional case, represented by the strip of elastic shown in Figure 22. Showing that uniform expansion of a one-dimensional universe naturally gives rise to the Hubble relationship should make the idea easier to carry over to the real, three-dimensional case.

Five time-steps are shown in Figure 22, each a billion years after the previous one, with the third time-step identified as 'today'. Moving from one time interval to the next, space (the strip of elastic) expands uniformly, and all the clusters of galaxies (the buttons) get farther apart. Imagine that cluster A is the Local Group of galaxies that contains the Milky Way and us. The separation of clusters A and B is 32 Mpc in the first image (represented by 32 mm on Figure 22), 36 Mpc in the second image, 40 Mpc in the third image, and so on. (Check these distances by measuring the separations of the 'clusters of galaxies' on Figure 22 if you wish.) So clusters A and B are receding from each other at a constant speed of 4 Mpc every billion years.

Similarly, to an astronomer in cluster A, cluster C appears at distances of 40 Mpc, 45 Mpc, 50 Mpc and so on moving down the sequence. So cluster C is getting farther away by 5 Mpc every billion years. This is a faster recession speed than that for cluster B, and is merely a consequence of it being farther away. There is more space between A and C than there is between A and B, so the expansion is greater, and the speed of separation is larger. To an astronomer in cluster A, cluster D appears at distances of 24 Mpc, 27 Mpc, 30 Mpc and so on moving down the sequence. So cluster D is getting farther away by 3 Mpc every billion years — slower than both

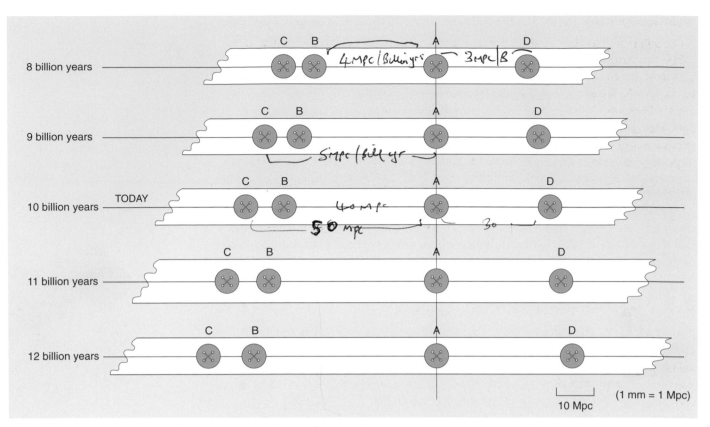

Figure 22   A model for the uniform expansion of part of a one-dimensional universe, shown at five time intervals, each a billion years after the previous one. The strip of elastic represents space and the buttons sewn onto it, labelled A to D, represent clusters of galaxies. As space expands uniformly so the clusters of galaxies all recede from each other. As explained in the text, the speed at which they recede increases with increasing separation from the point of measurement. The scale of this figure is 1 mm to 1 Mpc.

clusters B and C since it's nearer. There is less space between A and D than between either A and C or A and B, so the expansion is less, and the speed of separation is smaller.

The model works well for measurements from cluster A, which we can imagine to be the Local Group of galaxies, but how do things look to one of Douglas Adams' Amoeboid Zingatularian astronomers in cluster B? Well, to it, cluster A is clearly receding at the constant speed of 4 Mpc every billion years, but cluster C is receding at only 1 Mpc every billion years. And that's fine, because cluster C is much closer than cluster A and so has a smaller recession speed. Similarly, cluster D is receding from cluster B at a constant speed of 7 Mpc every billion years. And that too is just what would be expected, because cluster D is farther from cluster B than either A or C.

Wherever you happen to be in this one-dimensional universe, clusters that are farther away from you recede at larger and larger speeds, and the recession speed depends on the distance, just as described by the Hubble relationship. Furthermore, in the example here, the relative recession speed between any two clusters remains *constant* at all times.

The following example will help you to appreciate the relationships between recession speed, redshift, and the Hubble constant for the one-dimensional universe in Figure 22.

Worked example 2

(a) Imagine that you are an alien astronomer living on a planet, orbiting a star, in a galaxy in cluster D, making observations of galaxies in clusters A, B and C in Figure 22. Calculate the recession speeds, convert these into $km\,s^{-1}$ and then work out the redshifts of clusters A, B and C. (The speed of light is $3 \times 10^5\,km\,s^{-1}$, 1 Mpc is equivalent to $3 \times 10^{19}\,km$, and 1 year is equivalent to 3×10^7 seconds.)

(b) Using any of the three speeds you calculated in part (a), what is the value of the Hubble constant at the time identified as 'today' in this one-dimensional Universe? Express your answer in the unit $km\,s^{-1}\,Mpc^{-1}$.

(c) By carefully considering Figure 22, how does the value of the Hubble constant differ in the past and in the future of this one-dimensional Universe from the value calculated in part (b)?

Answer

(a) The speeds of recession of clusters A, B and C as measured from cluster D are 3 Mpc per billion years, 7 Mpc per billion years and 8 Mpc per billion years, respectively. The next step is to convert these speeds into $km\,s^{-1}$, because we need to compare these speeds with the speed of light, which we have in $km\,s^{-1}$.

Now, 1 Mpc is equivalent to $3 \times 10^{19}\,km$ and one billion years is equivalent to $(10^9\,years) \times (3 \times 10^7$ seconds per year$) = 3 \times 10^{16}\,s$. So a speed of 1 Mpc per billion years is roughly equal to $(3 \times 10^{19}\,km)/(3 \times 10^{16}\,s)$, which is $1000\,km\,s^{-1}$. This is a convenient conversion! The recession speeds of the three clusters are therefore about $3000\,km\,s^{-1}$, $7000\,km\,s^{-1}$ and $8000\,km\,s^{-1}$ respectively.

Using Equation 4b, redshift = speed of galaxy/speed of light, the redshifts of the three clusters as measured from cluster D, are:

redshift(A) $= 3000\,km\,s^{-1}/3 \times 10^5\,km\,s^{-1} = 0.010$

redshift(B) $= 7000\,km\,s^{-1}/3 \times 10^5\,km\,s^{-1} = 0.023$

redshift(C) $= 8000\,km\,s^{-1}/3 \times 10^5\,km\,s^{-1} = 0.027$

(b) Using any of the three speeds from part (a), the Hubble constant at the time identified as 'today' is found from Equation 5c as Hubble constant = speed of galaxy/distance to galaxy. So for the measurement of cluster C from cluster D, the Hubble constant is $8000\,km\,s^{-1}/80\,Mpc$, which is $100\,km\,s^{-1}\,Mpc^{-1}$. The Hubble constant is measured with the same value (at the same time) *wherever* you happen to be in this one-dimensional universe, and this is true of the universe that we find ourselves in too. This value of the Hubble constant is, however, somewhat higher than the current value in our Universe.

(c) At times in the past of this one-dimensional universe, clusters of galaxies were closer together, but moving apart at the same constant speed. So the Hubble constant at earlier times was *larger* than it is at the time identified as 'today'. Conversely, at times in the future of this one-dimensional universe, clusters of galaxies are farther apart, but still moving at the same constant speed. So the Hubble constant at later times will be *smaller* than it is at the time identified as 'today'.

In order to appreciate this more quantitatively, consider the value of the Hubble constant at the time indicated as 9 billion years. The recession speed of (say) cluster C from cluster D is still $8000\,km\,s^{-1}$, as calculated in part (a). This value is the same at *whatever time* we choose to measure it. The two clusters are 72 Mpc apart at this time. So the Hubble constant at this time is $(8000\,km\,s^{-1})/(72\,Mpc)$, which is $110\,km\,s^{-1}\,Mpc^{-1}$. Conversely, at the time indicated as 11 billion years, clusters C and D are 88 Mpc apart, so the Hubble constant at this time is $(8000\,km\,s^{-1})/(88\,Mpc)$, or $90\,km\,s^{-1}\,Mpc^{-1}$, which is smaller than it is at the time identified as 'today' in Figure 22.

Notice that in this universe, even though any particular pair of clusters of galaxies continue travelling apart at the same speed at all times, the rate of expansion of the intervening space becomes progressively smaller. The Hubble constant quantifies the expansion rate of the Universe, and clearly the expansion rate of this one-dimensional universe is slowing down. In our Universe too the Hubble constant is not the same at different times. ◀

What was demonstrated in one dimension with Figure 22 is also true in the real three-dimensional Universe in which we live; it's just a little harder to visualize, and we won't attempt to do so here.

Having interpreted the Hubble relationship to mean that space is expanding, we can now look at the consequences of this phenomenon. It is believed that the amount of matter in the Universe is constant. So, since the separation between distant galaxies is continually increasing, this implies that the mean density of the Universe — the mass per unit volume — is continuously falling.

> In other words, in the distant past the Universe was very dense, whereas now, the mean density is rather low. This is the first important piece of evidence about the conditions that prevailed in the early Universe.

3.6   Strange ideas

Figure 23

When discussing the overall structure of the Universe, some rather awkward questions often arise. In the discussion below these will be addressed in the hope that it will answer any questions you have about the behaviour of our expanding Universe. Before starting though, you should be warned that you will be required to put aside some 'common sense' notions of reality and accept a few ideas that may at first seem rather strange. As you will see, it is not only artists and poets who need fertile and wide-ranging imaginations — such characteristics are equally useful for cosmologists! Although some of these ideas require you to put aside common sense, be assured that the mathematical models describing the Universe are based firmly on Einstein's general theory of relativity (see Chapter 8) and are unambiguous.

The first complication is that the Hubble constant was larger in the distant past than it is today. There are two reasons for this. First, as you saw in the one-dimensional universe analogy (Worked example 2), even if galaxies keep moving apart with a constant speed, the Hubble constant decreases as time progresses simply because it is equal to speed divided by distance, and the distances keep getting larger. Second, the expansion rate of the Universe may be decreasing, owing to the gravitational attraction between all the matter in the Universe (more about this, however, in Chapter 12, where we consider whether the expansion rate may also increase …). This phenomenon is referred to as **deceleration**, and will further reduce the value of the Hubble constant as time progresses. The precise value of the deceleration is not known, so consequently the distance scale of the Universe in the past is also uncertain.

Also, a word of caution is called for concerning the relationships between redshift and speed that were developed earlier. Although Equations 4 and 5 are adequate for our discussion, it would be wrong to assume that they apply in every situation. In fact, they are only true when the recession speeds and distances involved are less than about 10% of the speed of light and 500 Mpc, respectively. At high recession speeds, the physical meaning of 'distance' in the Universe needs to be considered carefully. The light that we now see from rapidly receding galaxies was emitted by them when the Universe was much younger than it is now. In the time it has taken that light to reach us, the Universe has expanded and so distances between galaxies have changed. Therefore, care has to be taken in interpreting the distances and speeds that are measured in an expanding universe when the redshift is greater than about 0.1.

For these reasons, cosmologists don't usually refer to the speed and distance of rapidly receding, very distant galaxies, but to their redshift and **look-back time**. This latter quantity is the time taken for the light emitted by a galaxy to reach us, and indicates how far back in time we are seeing. Looking at objects far away means that we are actually looking back in time, because the light that we see was emitted by the object in the distant past, and has taken a substantial amount of time to reach us. For instance, assuming a Hubble constant of $72\,\mathrm{km\,s^{-1}\,Mpc^{-1}}$, it turns out that a galaxy with a redshift of 3 is situated at a look-back time of around 8 billion years. (The derivation of this value is beyond the scope of this course.) We are seeing the galaxy as it was 8 billion years ago, because it has taken that long for the light emitted by the galaxy to reach us.

Aside from these somewhat technical issues, the idea of an expanding Universe also throws up some rather strange concepts. In response to the claim that space is expanding uniformly, many people ask (not unreasonably) 'What is the Universe expanding into?' In fact, the expansion of the Universe is interpreted very differently from an expansion of matter *into* space; rather it is interpreted as an expansion *of space itself*. Space is a property of the Universe, and matter is (more or less) fixed in a space that expands. This was illustrated by the one-dimensional universe analogy of Figure 22: the elastic (space) expands uniformly, but the buttons (clusters of galaxies) remain the same size and shape, they are merely carried along by the universal expansion. Similarly, we are not expanding, nor is the Earth, the Solar System, the Milky Way, or even our Local Group of galaxies. These objects are all bound together by electric and gravitational forces of attraction between the atoms and molecules of which they are composed. Only beyond the scale of clusters of galaxies does the expansion win.

Although the redshift of distant galaxies has been described as being comparable to a Doppler shift, it is important to realize that there is one vital difference between a 'standard' Doppler redshift (such as that caused by speeding ambulances or the random motion of galaxies in the Local Group) and what may be called a 'cosmological' redshift. The Doppler effect is the result of the motion of an object *through* space at a certain speed, whereas cosmological redshifts are caused by the expansion *of* space itself. So, even though a distant cluster of galaxies may have a recession speed that is (say) 88% of the speed of light, that cluster is not moving rapidly with respect to its local surroundings. In terms of the analogy in Figure 22, the buttons on the strip of elastic are not moving with respect to the local patch of elastic. It is the expansion of space itself that 'stretches out' the wavelength of the emitted light as it travels through space. The more space there is between the object emitting the light and the point of observation, the bigger the 'stretch', and so the larger the redshift.

Another question that many people ask is 'Where in the Universe is the centre of this expansion?' Well, there is no centre of expansion — all space is expanding at the same rate in all directions, and the same expansion would be measured wherever you happened to be. Perhaps another analogy will help here. Figure 24 shows a two-dimensional universe — one step up in complexity from that shown in Figure 22,

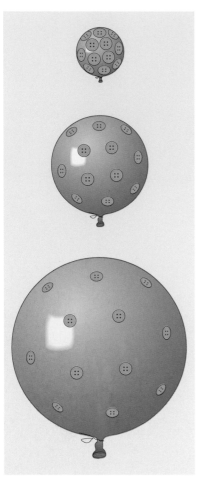

Figure 24 The expansion of a (finite) two-dimensional universe visualized as the surface of an inflating balloon. Notice that the centre of expansion does not lie anywhere in the two-dimensional space of this universe (the surface of the balloon).

but still one dimension short of the real thing. Here the universe is represented as the two-dimensional surface of a balloon, with the buttons stuck on the surface representing the clusters of galaxies as before. It is only the *surface* of this balloon that represents space — everything inside or outside the balloon is not part of this universe. As space expands (i.e. as the balloon is inflated), the clusters of galaxies move farther apart with their recession speeds increasing with distance just as in Figure 22. But the centre of expansion (the centre of the balloon) does not lie anywhere within the universe. Our own three-dimensional Universe also has no centre of expansion. The problem is that none of us can think in enough dimensions to visualize it properly.

This is an important point: do not even attempt to visualize the corresponding situation for our own three-dimensional Universe. It is simply not possible to do so!

Perhaps there is a simple answer to the question 'How big is the Universe?' Well, there is a simple answer, but it's not easy to comprehend. The Universe may be infinite in extent — *and may always have been so.* (The balloon analogy is therefore misleading in this respect, since that describes a Universe with finite size.) The Universe may have been infinite at the instant of its creation, and may have remained infinite ever since. When it is said that space is expanding, you should *not* interpret this to mean that the overall *size* of the Universe is increasing (if it's infinite it can't get any bigger since infinity is the biggest possible!). Rather, you should interpret it to mean that the *separation* of large structures within the Universe is increasing — in other words galaxies are getting farther apart. We shall return to this question in Section 12, when we consider the possible future behaviour of the Universe.

A popular misconception is to think of the Universe as originating at a 'point in space' and expanding from there. This is quite the wrong visual image, and you should try not to think in these terms. Remember, space is a property of the Universe, not something within which the Universe sits. Furthermore, the Big Bang theory implies that the entire infinite space of the Universe, and the raw materials from which the galaxies were built, were all created at the same instant. The separations between objects increase with time, as they are carried along by the expansion of the space that was created at the instant the Universe began. Again, don't even attempt to visualize an infinite, expanding three-dimensional Universe — it's simply impossible for anyone to do!

A final point is that there is no edge to the Universe either. Since the Universe may be infinite then, by definition, it goes on forever and travelling in a straight line you would never reach an edge. Even if the Universe were finite in size though, you would never reach an edge either. Travelling in a straight line in a finite Universe, you would eventually end up back where you started, just as an ant would crawling over the surface of the two-dimensional universe model in Figure 24.

The preceding few paragraphs provide a rather mind-bending excursion for most people! The problem is that we are only used to comprehending things on a much smaller scale of time and space than is necessary to properly grasp the immensity of the Universe. The ideas can be expressed mathematically, but would be an unnecessary and lengthy detour from the main story. Nevertheless, the basic ideas are not so difficult if you are prepared to discard some ideas that are 'common sense' in our everyday experience. To summarize,

- The Universe may be infinite, with no centre and no edge. It may always have been infinite, including at the instant of its creation in a Big Bang.

- It makes no sense to ask what is 'outside' the Universe, because space is a property of the Universe itself, and does not exist elsewhere.

- Space itself is expanding uniformly such that the separation between distant galaxies increases with time, and the overall density of the Universe decreases.

- A consequence of this uniform expansion is that the recession speed increases with increasing distance from the place of measurement.

3.7 The age of the Universe

For the time being, let's follow this first big clue of cosmology: space is expanding. We can imagine 'running the film backwards in time' and conclude that, in the past, all the galaxies were closer together than they are now. If we make the assumption that all the galaxies we can see have been moving at their present speeds since the Universe began, then we can use the Hubble constant to calculate a rough age for the Universe.

If the Hubble constant is $72 \text{ km s}^{-1} \text{ Mpc}^{-1}$, then two galaxies that are currently 500 Mpc apart have a recession speed between them of $(72 \text{ km s}^{-1} \text{ Mpc}^{-1} \times 500 \text{ Mpc})$ = $36\,000 \text{ km s}^{-1}$. (Remember, that's 72 km s^{-1} faster for every megaparsec farther apart.) So, if we imagine 'running the film backwards', these two galaxies would have been 'zero' distance apart at a certain time in the past. That time is given by $500 \text{ Mpc}/36\,000 \text{ km s}^{-1}$, since the time for a 'journey' is simply given by the distance travelled divided by the speed. But distance divided by speed is 1/(Hubble constant). So the quantity 1/(Hubble constant) provides a rough value for the age of the Universe, assuming that the expansion rate has been constant since time began.

Worked example 3

What is the age of the Universe?

Answer

The value of the Hubble constant currently accepted by most cosmologists is about 72 kilometres per second per megaparsec. To work out an age for the Universe, we first need to rationalize the units here somewhat. At the moment, the Hubble constant has a unit that includes two different units of distance: megaparsecs and kilometres. As we noted earlier, 1 Mpc is equal to about 3×10^{19} km, so we can re-write the value of the Hubble constant as:

$$\frac{72 \text{ kilometres per second}}{1 \text{ megaparsec}} = \frac{72 \text{ kilometres per second}}{3 \times 10^{19} \text{ kilometres}}$$

Hubble constant = 2.4×10^{-18} per second

An estimate for the age of the Universe is then 1/(Hubble constant), so

age = $1/(2.4 \times 10^{-18} \text{ per second}) = 4.2 \times 10^{17}$ seconds

Since one year is equivalent to about 3×10^7 seconds, expressing this time as an equivalent number of years results in a value of:

$$\text{age} = \frac{4.2 \times 10^{17} \text{ seconds}}{3 \times 10^7 \text{ seconds per year}} = 1.4 \times 10^{10} \text{ years or 14 billion years} \blacktriangleleft$$

In practice, the true age of the Universe will be somewhat different from the value given by 1/(Hubble constant), because the expansion of the Universe has *not* proceeded at a constant rate since time began. The current best estimate for the age of the Universe is 13.7 billion years.

3.8　Summary and questions

The electromagnetic spectrum extends from gamma-rays (short wavelength, high energy) through X-rays, ultraviolet, visible light, infrared, and microwaves to radio waves (long wavelength, low energy).

Although electromagnetic radiation travels from place to place like a wave, it interacts with matter in the form of a stream of particles, called photons.

When an atom makes a transition from one energy level to another, a photon is either absorbed or emitted. The energy of the photon is exactly equal to the difference in energy between the two energy levels involved. Since each atom has a specific range of energy levels, each type of atom gives rise to a characteristic spectrum of emission lines or absorption lines.

The distance from the Local Group to a cluster of galaxies may be determined using the relationship between the brightness of its tenth brightest member and the standard luminosity of that galaxy.

The procedure is based on the assumption that the tenth brightest galaxies in all clusters have the *same* luminosity. Distances to galaxies and clusters of galaxies are measured in the units kiloparsecs, megaparsecs and gigaparsecs.

The redshift of a galaxy is defined as the shift in the wavelength of a spectral line seen in its spectrum, divided by the rest wavelength of that line.

The recession speed of a distant galaxy is equal to its redshift multiplied by the speed of light.

All galaxies beyond the Local Group exhibit redshifts, so all distant galaxies are receding from us. Moreover, the recession speed is greater for galaxies that are further away. The Hubble relationship states that the recession speed is equal to the Hubble constant multiplied by the distance away.

The Hubble constant is measured to be around $72 \text{ km s}^{-1} \text{ Mpc}^{-1}$.

The Hubble relationship is a consequence of the fact that space itself is expanding uniformly. Since the separation of distant objects is increasing with time, the mean density of the Universe is continually falling. Extrapolating the observed expansion back in time leads us to believe that the Universe originated about 14 billion years ago.

The Universe may be infinite in size, and may always have been; it has no centre, since the same expansion would be measured from any location within it; it has no edge because space is a property of the Universe itself and does not exist elsewhere.

Question 6

(a) Which model of light is used to explain (i) the way it travels through space and *wave* (ii) its interaction with atoms? *particle*

(b) Arrange the following types of electromagnetic radiation in order of (i) increasing photon energy and (ii) increasing wavelength: blue light, gamma-rays, infrared radiation, yellow light, microwaves, radio waves, red light, ultraviolet radiation, X-rays.

*(i) Radio
Micro
Infra-red
red
yellow
blue
ultra-violet
X-rays
gamma rays*

*(ii) gamma
X-rays
Ultra-Violet
blue
yellow
red
infra-red
micro
Radio*

(c) If an electron and a positron at rest mutually annihilate each other to produce a pair of photons, (i) what would be the energy of each photon and (ii) in which part of the electromagnetic spectrum would these photons lie? ◄

*(i) 500 keV = 5×10^5 keV
(ii) Boundary X-rays γ rays*

Question 7

The spectral distribution of the light from a sodium street lamp is an emission line spectrum consisting primarily of two spectral lines, very close together, in the yellow part of the visible spectrum, as shown in Figure 25. Make a rough sketch of the spectral distribution corresponding to light from a tungsten filament light bulb, after it has passed through cool sodium vapour. ◄

Figure 25 The spectral distribution of the light from a sodium street lamp.

Question 8

A cluster of galaxies is said to be at a distance of 200 Mpc from the Earth.

(a) What is this distance in kilometres? *$200 \times 3 \times 10^{19}$ km $= 6 \times 10^{21}$ km*

(b) How long would it take a beam of light to travel from the cluster to the Earth? ◄
$= \dfrac{6 \times 10^{21}}{3 \times 10^5} = 2 \times 10^{16}$ sec $= 2/3 \times 10^9$ yrs $= 2/3$ billion yrs

Question 9

A fast jet aircraft has a red light on its tail that emits light with a wavelength of 656 nm. The aircraft travels away from you at a speed of 0.6 km s^{-1} (about twice the speed of sound).

(a) What would be the redshift of the light reaching you from the tail of the aircraft?
*$0.6 = r \times 3 \times 10^5$
$\Rightarrow r = \dfrac{3 \times 10^5}{0.6}$ $\dfrac{0.6}{3 \times 10^5} = \dfrac{3}{5 \times 3 \times 10^5}$
$2 \times 10^{-6} = \dfrac{1}{5 \times 10^5}$*

(b) What would be the shift in wavelength of the light that you observe? (You may assume that the speed of light is 3×10^5 km s^{-1}.) ◄
*shift $= 5 \times 10^{-5} \times 656$
$= 1.3 \times 10^{-2}$ 2×10^{-6}*

Question 10

The spectrum of light from a distant galaxy contains absorption lines that are identified as being due to hydrogen atoms. A particular line is observed at a wavelength of 500.7 nm, compared with the wavelength of 486.1 nm that would be produced by a source at rest in the laboratory.

(a) Is the galaxy receding from or approaching towards the Earth? *receding*

(b) What is the value of the redshift or blueshift for the galaxy? *r.s. $= 14.6/486.1 = 0.03$*

(c) What is the speed of the galaxy with respect to the Earth? (You may assume that the speed of light is 3×10^5 km s^{-1}.) ◄
r.s $= \dfrac{\text{galaxy speed}}{c}$ $\Rightarrow$ $0.03 = \dfrac{GS}{3 \times 10^5}$ $\Rightarrow GS = 9000$ km s^{-1}

Question 11

Assume that the Hubble constant is 72 km s^{-1} Mpc^{-1} and the speed of light is 3×10^5 km s^{-1}.

(a) What would be the redshift of a galaxy at a distance of 400 Mpc from the Local Group?
$H = \dfrac{S}{d}$ $\Rightarrow$ $72 = \dfrac{S}{400}$ $\Rightarrow S = 2.88 \times 10^4$ km s^{-1}

(b) What would be the distance to a galaxy that has a redshift of 0.12?

[Hint: Calculate the recession speed of the galaxy first.] ◄
r.s $= \dfrac{2.88 \times 10^4}{3 \times 10^5}$ = 9.6×10^{-2}

(a) $0.12 = \dfrac{S}{3 \times 10^5}$ $\Rightarrow S = 3.6 \times 10^4$ (b) $72 = \dfrac{3.6 \times 10^4}{d}$ $\Rightarrow d = 500$ Mpc

49

4 The cooling Universe

Time flies like an arrow. Fruit flies like a banana.

Groucho Marx, 1890–1977

Having looked closely at the expansion of the Universe, we will now examine the second major piece of evidence for an evolving Universe, namely the observation that the Universe is gradually cooling.

A discussion of the fact that the Universe is cooling implies that the Universe must have a temperature, and that may seem a rather strange concept. It makes sense to talk about the temperature at the centre or surface of the Sun or the Earth, but what is the temperature of the Universe as a whole? After all, nowadays the Universe largely consists of almost empty space between the galaxies. However, space is not as empty as you might suppose. Even away from stars and galaxies, space still contains electromagnetic radiation. On average, every cubic metre of space contains about 400 million photons! These photons constitute the 'heat radiation' of the Universe and their spectrum corresponds to a particular temperature.

4.1 Black-body radiation

We begin by considering the question, what *is* temperature? Roughly speaking, as an object becomes hotter, the atoms and molecules of which it is composed move around or vibrate more rapidly. As an object cools down, its atoms and molecules move around or vibrate ever more slowly. There will come a point when the atoms and molecules cease moving altogether, and such an object would then be at the absolute coldest temperature possible. Because there is such a thing as an absolute minimum temperature, in many areas of science, the most useful way to describe temperatures is to use the **absolute temperature** scale. This is also known as the kelvin temperature scale, in honour of William Thomson, Lord Kelvin (1824–1907) who developed the idea in 1848. On this scale, zero kelvin (0 K) is the coldest temperature possible.

Zero kelvin corresponds to about −273 °C on the more familiar celsius scale, and a temperature interval of 1 K is identical with an interval of 1 °C. A comparison between the kelvin and celsius temperature scales is shown in Figure 26. As you can see, the melting temperature of ice (0 °C) is equivalent to about 273 K and the boiling temperature of water (100 °C) is equivalent to about 373 K.

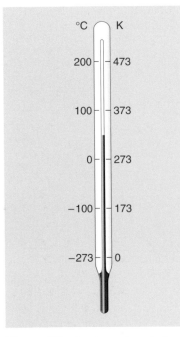

Figure 26 A comparison between the kelvin and celsius temperature scales.

⬤ What is a typical room temperature on the kelvin temperature scale?

◯ 20 °C, which is 293 K.

When a hot-plate on an electric cooker is heated up, it glows 'red-hot' and radiates energy in the form of photons. These photons have a range of energies but the precise distribution of photons — the relative number that are emitted with any particular energy — depends on the temperature of the hot-plate. As you know, the distribution of photons plotted against photon energy is simply the spectrum of the radiation, as you saw in Figure 14. It turns out, quite reasonably, that as the temperature of an object increases, so it emits photons of higher and higher energies. There will still be a distribution of photons with different energies, but the average, or *mean* photon energy will shift to higher values. An object whose emission has a mean photon energy in the blue part of the spectrum (about 3 eV) will be hotter than one whose emission has a mean photon energy in the red part of the spectrum (about 2 eV), for instance. But there is no need to restrict this relationship between photon energy and temperature to merely the visible part of the electromagnetic spectrum. At higher energies (shorter wavelengths) than blue light there are the ultraviolet and X-ray regions. Objects whose emission has a mean photon energy in these parts of the spectrum must be extremely hot. Conversely, at lower energies (longer wavelengths) than red light are the infrared and microwave regions. Emission that has a mean photon energy in these ranges would indicate much lower temperatures.

As a rough rule of thumb, a body at a temperature of around 3000 K gives rise to photons whose mean energy is about 1 eV, and the mean energy of the photons emitted by other bodies is proportional to the temperature.

So we may write,

mean photon energy in electronvolts = temperature in kelvin/3000   (6a)

or alternatively

temperature in kelvin = mean photon energy in electronvolts × 3000   (6b)

○ What is the mean energy of photons radiated by objects at a typical room temperature?

○ A typical room temperature is about 300 K. This is ten times less than the 3000 K that gives a mean photon energy of 1 eV. So the mean photon energy must be about 0.1 eV. This corresponds to the infrared part of the electromagnetic spectrum.

○ To get X-ray photons of mean energy 100 keV what temperature is required?

○ 100 keV = 100 000 eV, so a temperature of around 100 000 × 3000 K = 300 million kelvin is required.

The continuous spectral distributions of many objects have precisely the same shape, they are merely shifted to different energies or wavelengths. Some examples are shown in Figure 27, and each of these is what is known as a **black-body spectrum** or **thermal spectrum**.

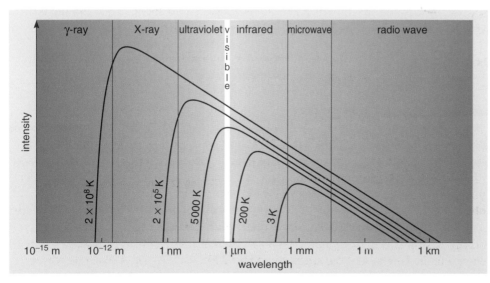

Figure 27 The black-body spectra emitted by objects at temperatures of 2×10^8 K, 2×10^5 K, 5000 K, 200 K and 3 K. The scale along the bottom shows the wavelength of the radiation, and you can see that hotter objects emit more of their radiation at shorter wavelengths. Note that the wavelengths and intensities are plotted on 'powers-of-ten' scales to allow a vast range to be included in one diagram.

From everyday experience, you may be aware that a black surface absorbs more radiation than a silver surface. In fact, a perfectly black surface will absorb all the radiation that falls upon it and, in a steady-state (or equilibrium) situation where it maintains a constant temperature, it will also emit all this radiation back again. (We are assuming that the surface is in a vacuum and cannot exchange energy with its surroundings in any other way.) The phrase 'black body' is therefore used as a shorthand to describe any object that behaves as a perfect absorber and emitter of radiation. The crucial features of black-body spectra are that they all have the same continuous shape, they contain no emission or absorption lines, and the mean photon energy (or corresponding wavelength) depends *only* on the temperature of the object according to Equation 6.

The key to understanding how black-body spectra are produced is that the object and the radiation are in **thermal equilibrium**. As much radiation is being absorbed as is being emitted at every instant, and the object therefore remains at a constant temperature. We can therefore say that the radiation also possesses this same temperature. The conditions necessary to create such a situation are generally those of high temperatures and large amounts of energy. Under such conditions, photons are rapidly absorbed and re-emitted by matter.

○ In order for a photon to be absorbed by an atom, what condition must be met with regard to the energy levels of the atom?

○ There must be a pair of energy levels whose separation is equal to the energy of the photon concerned.

○ How could you guarantee that a photon of virtually *any* energy could be absorbed?

○ There must be a great many energy levels, very close together, and extending over a large range of energy.

It turns out that this situation will exist when atoms are ionized (i.e. when one or more electrons are removed from an atom), and also when atoms are arranged in a metal. So, in either of these cases, photons of *all* energies may be absorbed and emitted, and a continuous spectrum is produced. The continuous spectrum of the Sun and other stars (ignoring the absorption lines superimposed on top) may be approximated by black-body spectra.

4.2   The cosmic microwave background

Objects in the Universe emit electromagnetic radiation across the whole spectrum from radio waves through infrared, visible radiation, ultraviolet, and X-rays to gamma-rays. The spectra from individual objects are, in some cases, characteristic of thermal processes, and so have the continuous black-body shape. If astronomers observe the Universe in the microwave part of the spectrum — that is at wavelengths of a few millimetres — a remarkable phenomenon is observed. What they detect is a background microwave 'glow' coming from the whole Universe, and wherever they look (away from individual stars or galaxies) it has virtually the same spectral distribution and intensity. Moreover, the shape of the spectrum is that of a thermal or black-body source. This **cosmic microwave background**, or CMB, was discovered in 1964 by Arno Penzias and Robert Wilson (Figure 28).

Figure 28   Wilson and Penzias standing by the antenna with which they discovered the cosmic microwave background at Bell Telephone Laboratories in New Jersey, USA. They were tracking a satellite and found that their antenna picked up not only the signal from the satellite, but also some background 'noise'. What they discovered was that this noise came from all over the sky. After consultations with physicists from Princeton University, they realized that they had inadvertently discovered the 'heat radiation' of the Universe. Their work played a major part in establishing the standard model of the origin and early evolution of the Universe.

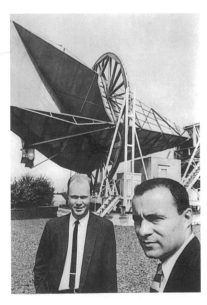

Over the years since Penzias and Wilson first discovered the CMB, its spectrum and variation across the sky have been investigated and mapped with increasing accuracy. Some of the most recent, and accurate, measurements are those made using the Cosmic Background Explorer (COBE) satellite, which was launched in 1989. The average spectrum of the radiation, over the whole sky, measured by COBE is shown in Figure 29. The observations are an excellent fit with the theoretical curve that would be expected from a black-body source at a temperature of 2.73 K. Sometimes, this value is quoted approximately as simply 3 K.

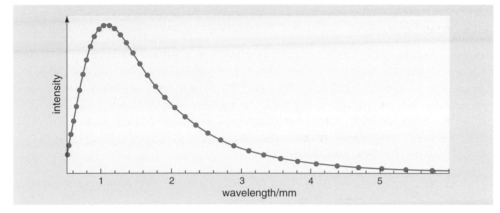

Figure 29   The spectrum of the cosmic microwave background radiation as measured by COBE. The points are the measured data, and the line drawn through them is a black-body spectrum corresponding to a temperature of 2.73 K. The wavelength corresponding to the mean photon energy of the spectrum is about 2 mm. (Notice that whereas Figure 27 was drawn on a powers-of-ten scale in order to display the vast range of wavelengths across the electromagnetic spectrum, this graph is plotted on a simple linear scale. For this reason the shape of the spectrum here appears different from that of the black-body spectra in Figure 27.)

In precise physical terms, the temperature of the CMB radiation is now (coincidentally!) one hundred times colder than the normal melting temperature of ice (i.e. 273 K). Yet, the spectrum has exactly the same shape as is observed in, say, a furnace whose walls are a thousand times hotter at a temperature of 3000 K, where interactions between radiation and matter rapidly create the stable distribution of photon energies necessary to produce a black-body spectrum. The temperature 3000 K can be thought of as roughly the *minimum* at which atoms and radiation can interact significantly. Below this temperature the energy levels in hydrogen atoms are simply too far apart to absorb many of the photons corresponding to a black-body spectrum.

At a temperature of only about 3 K, a steady state, or thermal equilibrium between matter and radiation in the Universe is virtually impossible to establish since the energy of most of the photons is so very small when compared with the separation of energy levels in hydrogen atoms. So how can radiation that is now far too cold to interact with matter, to any significant extent, have acquired a thermal spectrum, when thermal spectra are generally characteristic of processes at least a thousand times hotter? Were it not for the previous observation of an expanding Universe, there would be a real puzzle here.

If you take any sample of gas and allow it to expand, without putting any energy in or taking any out, the temperature of the gas will fall. Now, the Universe may be thought of as just such a sample of gas. As the Universe grows older, so space expands.

No energy is put into or removed from the Universe, so the overall temperature of the Universe naturally falls with time. Bearing this in mind, the solution to the problem above is rather simple: when the CMB radiation was last in equilibrium with matter in the Universe, it was a thousand times hotter. The thousand-fold cooling since then was produced by the expansion of the Universe (or, more properly, of space itself). In other words, the CMB radiation we now see was emitted by matter at a time in the distant past when the Universe was much hotter than it is today.

Another (entirely equivalent) way to look at this is in terms of redshift. As the CMB radiation travels towards us from distant parts of the Universe, so the wavelength of the radiation is redshifted by the expansion of the intervening space. Looking back to the time when the CMB radiation and matter were last in equilibrium with each other entails a redshift of about one thousand. In other words, the wavelength corresponding to the mean photon energy of the CMB radiation that we see today (about 2 mm) was a thousand times shorter (i.e. it was about 2 μm) when the radiation was emitted. The wavelength of the radiation has been 'stretched out' by the expansion of the Universe. A lengthening of the wavelength from 2 μm to 2 mm corresponds to a reduction in photon energy from 1 eV to 0.001 eV. So the expansion of the Universe has shifted the mean photon energy of the radiation, from the infrared part of the spectrum into the microwave region, where it is observed today.

> The CMB radiation is therefore a relic of the time when radiation and matter in the Universe existed in equilibrium, at a temperature of around 3000 K. The CMB photons pervade the entire Universe, wherever astronomers look. This indicates that the entire Universe was once at a much higher temperature.

A comparison between conditions in the Universe when the CMB radiation was produced and conditions today is given in Table 7.

Table 7 A comparison between conditions in the Universe when the CMB radiation was produced and conditions today.

	Conditions when the CMB was produced	Conditions today
temperature of the Universe	3000 K	3 K
mean wavelength of radiation	2 μm	2 mm
mean photon energy	1 eV	0.001 eV
spectral region	infrared	microwave
redshift	1000	0

4.3 The hot big bang model

The expansion of the Universe (as expressed by the Hubble relationship) tells us that objects in the Universe were closer together in the past than they are today. In other words, the Universe was denser in the past than it is now. The cosmic microwave background radiation tells us that the Universe was hotter in the past than it is now. These are the two main pieces of evidence pointing to the fact that our Universe originated in what has become known as a **Big Bang**. The standard model for the origin and early evolution of the Universe is sometimes known as the hot big bang model. Space and time were created in this event, and space has expanded as time has progressed ever since. The story of the evolution of the Universe from the time of the Big Bang to the present day and beyond will be presented in Chapters 11 and 12. However, in order to discuss such an immense topic, it is necessary to appreciate the roles that four fundamental interactions each play in the evolution of the Universe. In Part II you will learn about these four interactions in turn, and you will discover how attempts are being made to unify these into a single, coherent, theory of everything.

4.4 Summary and questions

The radiation emitted by an object in thermal equilibrium has a black-body spectrum, and this continuous spectrum has a characteristic shape. The mean photon energy of a black-body spectrum is determined solely by the temperature of the body — higher temperature objects have spectra with a higher mean photon energy. A temperature of 3000 K corresponds roughly to a mean photon energy of 1 eV.

Wherever astronomers look in the Universe they see a 'glow' of radiation known as the cosmic microwave background (CMB). The black-body spectrum of this radiation corresponds to a temperature of about 3 K. This radiation has been redshifted to longer wavelengths (cooler temperatures) by the expansion of the Universe and indicates that the Universe was much hotter in the past than it is now.

The expansion and cooling of the Universe point to the fact that the Universe was both denser and hotter in the past. It is believed that time and space were created in an event referred to as the Big Bang.

Question 12

Use Figure 27 to help you to answer the following questions.

(a) A domestic oven can reach a temperature of around 230 °C. What is the equivalent temperature in kelvin, and in which region of the electromagnetic spectrum would the peak intensity of its black-body spectrum occur?

503 K
infrared

(b) The black-body spectrum emitted by an object has a peak intensity in the ultraviolet part of the electromagnetic spectrum. Roughly what is the temperature of the object? ◄

2×10^5 K

PART II
What rules does the Universe follow?

In Chapter 11 you will get a fuller picture of what the Universe was (most probably) like when the cosmic background radiation interacted readily with matter (long before the formation of the first galaxies and stars). It is even possible to give a reasonable account of much earlier epochs in which the atoms, nuclei, leptons and quarks came into existence. But first, we need to summarize what is known about the interactions of matter and radiation, from experiments performed at energies achievable on Earth. These in turn suggest some things that might occur at energies higher than those we can achieve on Earth, but which were probably very common in the early Universe.

So we need to continue our investigations in the realm of the structure of the atom. This reflects the dramatic interplay between cosmology and particle physics in recent decades: each informs the other. Cosmologists have learned things from studying the cosmic microwave background radiation that challenge particle physicists to conjecture about interactions of particles at energies higher than those achievable in the laboratory. Particle physicists extrapolate their understanding of theories developed to explain laboratory results and then turn back to the Universe for evidence against which to test these theories.

○ Which two observed features of the Universe, described in Chapters 3 and 4, suggest that in its past it would have been a good laboratory for particle physics?

○ The Universe is expanding (Chapter 3) and cooling (Chapter 4), so in the past it was denser and hotter, and particle interactions would have been more frequent and more violent.

In Chapter 11 you will find that information from particle physics is needed to tell the best current version of the history of our Universe. It turns out that what is needed is a quantum theory of the interactions — or forces — between particles, and an understanding of how they change their character when the participating particles interact at high kinetic energies. In outlining this, we shall refer to **four fundamental interactions**, as follows:

1 **Electromagnetic interactions**: these are responsible for the forces between electrons and protons in atoms, and for the emission and absorption of electromagnetic radiation, such as light. A small leftover electromagnetic interaction of the electrons and protons in atoms allows atoms to bind together to make molecules and so is responsible for chemistry.

2 **Strong interactions**: these provide the (very) strong force between quarks *inside* protons and neutrons. A small residual strong interaction between quarks binds protons and neutrons together in the nuclei of atoms.

3 **Weak interactions**: these are responsible for processes, such as radioactive beta-decay, that involve both quarks and leptons.

4 **Gravitational interactions**: these make apples fall, maintain planets in their orbits around stars, and slow down the expansion of the Universe. However, they are negligible within the atom. But when matter aggregates into huge (and electrically neutral) lumps, such as planets and stars, gravity holds sway. You will see that it also holds some surprises, undreamt of by Newton.

These four interactions are the subjects of Chapters 5–8. We will look at the way in which these interactions operate, and also at how their strengths may be characterized. In Chapter 9 you will study the four interactions at work in our local power station, the Sun, and in Chapter 10 you will learn that these interactions are not as distinct as had been previously supposed. Some (perhaps all) of them may be different aspects of a more unified description of nature, appearing to us as different as ice, water, and steam, yet deriving from the same basic principles.

Remember, our aim is to understand how the Universe works. To do this we need to know about the different stages involved in building up nuclei, atoms, planets, stars and galaxies out of the material that emerged from the Big Bang. The key to all these processes is understanding the four fundamental interactions that govern the behaviour of the contents of the Universe. We will begin by relating familiar phenomena to the four interactions.

Question 13

For each of the following processes, identify a principal role played by one of the four fundamental interactions. If possible, give examples of roles played by one or more of the other three in each case. (a) A child bouncing on a trampoline. (b) Turning on an electric light in a darkened room. (c) Sunbathing. (d) Cancer therapies, such as chemotherapy and radiotherapy. ◀

(a) gravity
(b) electromagnetic
(c) electromagnetic
(d) electromagnetic

5 Electromagnetic interactions

> There are forces in nature called Love and Hate. The force of Love causes elements to be attracted to each other and to be built up into some particular form or person, and the force of Hate causes the decomposition of things.
>
> Empedocles, 430 BC

The behaviour of particles within atoms and molecules involves the interaction between charged particles, such as that which occurs between electrons and protons in an atom. These electromagnetic interactions, which are at the origin of all atomic and molecular activity, have two aspects: electric forces between charged objects, and magnetic forces between moving charges (i.e. electric currents). Electromagnetic radiation (such as light) is emitted or absorbed (as photons) in processes involving these forces.

These three features of electromagnetic interactions — electric forces, magnetic forces, and electromagnetic radiation — will now feature in turn in the rest of this Chapter. Our aim is to develop a thumbnail sketch of their unification, in the modern theory of quantum electrodynamics (QED).

5.1 Electric forces

The law describing the force of electrical attraction and repulsion was discovered by Charles Augustin de Coulomb in 1785 (Figure 30), and can be expressed as follows:

> **Coulomb's law**: Two particles of unlike (or like) charge, at rest, attract (or repel) each other with an electric force that is proportional to the product of their electric charges divided by the square of their separation.

Coulomb's law is therefore another example of an inverse square law, just like the relationship between brightness and luminosity introduced in Chapter 3.

Another aspect of Coulomb's law is that if one particle has a positive charge and the other has a negative charge (i.e. unlike charges) there is a positive force of attraction. Conversely, if the particles have charges with the same sign (both positive or both negative), the force between them is repulsive. In other words, unlike charges attract, and like charges repel each other.

Let's explore further what Coulomb's law implies about the forces between charged particles.

- If the charge of one particle doubles, what happens to the force between the two charged particles?

- The force also doubles, since it is proportional to the charge.

- If two charged particles are moved twice as far apart, what happens to the force between them?

- The force is reduced by a factor of four, since it depends on dividing by the square of the separation.

Figure 30 Charles Augustin de Coulomb (1736–1806) was a French physicist who worked on many areas of science, although it is for his work on electric forces that he is best remembered. He developed the inverse square law for describing electrical attraction and repulsion, which led to the definition of the electric charge.

We may also use Coulomb's law to investigate the strength of attraction between particles, such as protons and electrons. The result of such a calculation is remarkable. The electric force between a proton and an electron at the typical separation that applies within a hydrogen atom is equivalent to about 1% of the weight of a grain of sand. Yet a grain of sand contains around 10^{20} atoms. Now, the weight of an object is a measure of the gravitational force of attraction between the Earth and the object in question. So the electric force between a proton and electron is about the same size as the gravitational force between the Earth and 10^{18} atoms! From this you can see that the gravitational force exerted by the Earth on a *single* atom is utterly negligible compared with the electric forces within it.

5.2 The fine structure constant

One aim of this Chapter is to characterize the strength of the electrical interaction in a way that will be of universal significance, rather than simply comparing it with something else, like the weight of a grain of sand. A simple way to do this is to compare two energies, each of which relate to electrical interactions and each of which has a fundamental significance in the Universe.

The approach in the following paragraph may seem like a rather convoluted mathematical trick, but there is no need to worry, the important point is the bottom line of it all, boxed below. If you prefer not to worry about *how* the value for the strength of electrical interactions is calculated, then please just skip to the last two sentences of the following paragraph.

To characterize the strength of the electrical interaction, the first number we calculate is the electrical (potential) energy that exists between an electron and a positron, multiplied by their distance apart. The second number is obtained by multiplying the energy of a photon by the wavelength of electromagnetic radiation corresponding to that same part of the electromagnetic spectrum. Notice that both of these numbers are given as: energy × distance. Dividing the first number by the second, and then multiplying by another universal constant of nature, namely 'two pi' (which is the circumference of a circle divided by its radius), the answer is about 1/137. Because of the way we defined this number, the value is the same *whatever* units we use for energy and distance (provided we use the same units for both energies and for both distances) and *whatever* part of the electromagnetic spectrum or *whatever* separation of the electron and positron we use! The number, 1/137, is usually represented by the Greek letter alpha (α) and is referred to as the **fine structure constant** (for reasons that will become apparent later). Therefore we can say that the characteristic strength of electrical interactions in the Universe is

$$\alpha_{em} = 1/137$$

Often, in what follows, we shall be even more approximate and only quote the value of the fine structure constant to the nearest **order of magnitude** (i.e. the nearest power of ten). In these terms, the characteristic strength of electrical interactions is about $\alpha_{em} \sim 0.01$ (or 10^{-2}).

As we saw earlier, it is a basic principle of cosmology that the same laws, with the same fundamental constants, apply throughout all regions of the Universe, at all times. The distance between the crests of an electromagnetic wave may increase,

(a)

(b)

Figure 31 (a) Hans Christian Oersted (1777–1851) was a Danish physicist who, in 1820, discovered that an electric current produces a magnetic field. (b) André Ampère (1775–1836) was a French mathematician, physicist, philosopher and chemist who played a fundamental part in founding the science of electromagnetism.

significantly, during its transit over cosmological distances and times, because of the expansion of the Universe, but at the same time the photon energy decreases owing to redshift. We assume that the product of photon energy and wavelength was, is, and always will be the same fundamental constant throughout the Universe. Similarly, the value for the electrical potential energy between a positron and electron multiplied by the distance between them, at any point in the Universe, is assumed to be the same as the value found on Earth. Different units for energy and distance may certainly be used elsewhere in the Universe. However, dividing one quantity by the other will give a number that is independent of the actual units used. So when we calculate a dimensionless number, as for the fine structure constant, we obtain a number of universal significance, that characterizes the strength of electromagnetic interactions throughout the Universe, and on which everyone agrees.

5.3 Magnetic forces

Magnetism may be most familiar to you from the interaction of magnetic materials, such as a bar magnet and a compass needle. The magnetic properties of metals derive, however, from the motion of the electrons that they contain. Nowadays, perhaps the commonest source of 'moving electrons' is any electrical apparatus, for an electric current is simply that: a flow of electrons.

Around 1820, Hans Christian Oersted (Figure 31a) observed that an electric current flowing in a wire affects a compass needle placed close to it, thus demonstrating that the movement of charge produces a magnetic force, registered by the magnetic material in the compass needle. The converse effect is that a bar magnet exerts a magnetic force on moving charges. A dramatic demonstration (which you should *not* attempt yourself, lest it damage your equipment) is to bring a powerful magnet near to a television set, or computer screen. The current of electrons in the television tube is deflected, thereby distorting the image on the screen. A simpler demonstration is to dispense with magnetic materials entirely and study the (rather feeble) forces exerted by one electric current on another. The easiest situation to study involves two parallel wires, carrying currents, separated by a certain distance. In the 1820s, André Ampère (Figure 31b) showed that if the currents flow in the same direction, the wires attract each other; if they flow in opposite directions, there is a repulsion (Figure 32).

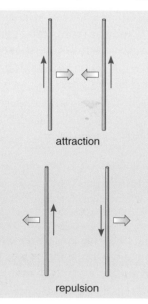

attraction

repulsion

Magnetic forces between wires are small and so are not easily detected. To make useful technological devices, magnetic materials, such as iron, are combined with current-carrying wires to produce electric motors. But long before these devices revolutionized technology, James Clerk Maxwell made a profound theoretical prediction, without which the nature of light itself would have remained obscure.

Figure 32 When the currents flow in the same direction, the wires attract; when the currents are opposite, they repel each other.

5.4 Electromagnetic radiation

In 1873, James Clerk Maxwell (Figure 33) unified the laws of magnetism with those of electricity, to produce his electromagnetic theory, with the distinctive prediction that light is a form of **electromagnetic radiation**.

As you have just seen, Coulomb had shown that *stationary* electric charges give rise to *electric* forces. A little later, Oersted and Ampère had shown that *moving* charges (i.e. electric currents) give rise to *magnetic* forces. The next discovery in this area was made around 1830, independently by Michael Faraday and Joseph Henry (Figure 34). They observed that a *changing* magnetic force produces an electric force. This phenomenon is called electromagnetic induction and is the basis of the simple dynamo, the principle of which is illustrated in Figure 35.

Maxwell's great contribution to the field of electricity and magnetism was to predict a further phenomenon: that a *changing* electric force produces a magnetic force. The previous three parts of electromagnetic theory had been developed in response to experiments. There was, it seemed, no data crying out for Maxwell's fourth idea. However, Maxwell's prediction was dramatic in the extreme: according to his equations, an *electromagnetic wave* could be set up, which would travel through a vacuum (i.e. empty space) with the universal (constant) speed: $3 \times 10^8 \, \text{m s}^{-1}$, which is

Figure 33 James Clerk Maxwell (1831–1879), was born in Edinburgh and was one of the greatest theoretical physicists of the 19th century. His 'Treatise on Electricity and Magnetism', published in 1873, explained all of the then known effects of electromagnetism and predicted the existence of 'electromagnetic waves' that travel at the speed of light. Maxwell suggested that such waves existed beyond the infrared and ultraviolet regions of the spectrum, but unfortunately didn't live to see his prediction verified in 1888, when Heinrich Hertz produced radio waves.

(a)

(b)

Figure 34 (a) Michael Faraday (1791–1867) was Britain's finest experimental scientist and its most distinguished popularizer of science. (b) Joseph Henry (1797–1878) was an American physicist noted for his early experiments in electromagnetic induction.

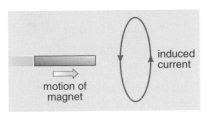

Figure 35 An example of electromagnetic induction. When a magnet is brought swiftly towards a loop of wire, a current is produced in the loop. The explanation is that the changing magnetic force, caused by moving the bar magnet, acts on the wire and sets up an electric force that causes electrons to move along the wire.

also the speed of light. In other words, Maxwell had not only thrown new light on light itself, but suggested the existence of electromagnetic radiation of *any* wavelength. It fell to Heinrich Hertz to provide the crucial experimental confirmation, in the late 1880s. Hertz also found that the familiar properties of light, involving reflection at a surface, and change of direction when passing through a prism or lens, were shown by electromagnetic waves of much longer wavelength. Guglielmo Marconi developed the technology which used radio waves as a practical means of communication.

Maxwell's equations of electromagnetism are the basis for telecommunications, electric motors and generators, waveguides that transport electromagnetic energy, radar navigation, and a host of other things which technology has harnessed to satisfy human demands. When you next use your home computer, spare a thought for the electric and magnetic forces that guide electrons through the computer's display unit, and for the light that carries the message from the screen to your retina. Maxwell's equations describe both parts of the process.

5.5 Quantum electrodynamics

Maxwell completed his theory of electromagnetism in 1873, and you may be wondering whether that was the last word on this phenomenon. In fact, it was not by a long way. The quantum physics of atoms is inextricably linked with the emission and absorption of electromagnetic radiation (photons). So clearly there was a need to unite Maxwell's theory of electromagnetism with the quantum model of the atom if a correct description of atoms and radiation was to be obtained. Another important development in physics in the early part of the 20th century was Einstein's **special theory of relativity**, published in 1905. A key result of this theory is that the kinetic energies of particles travelling at a substantial fraction of the speed of light become modified with respect to the conventional formula that applies in everyday situations. Electrons in atoms have a range of possible speeds, and there is a certain probability of finding an electron with *any* speed inside an atom. For example, the most probable speed for the electron in a hydrogen atom is around 1% of the speed of light, and even at this speed the conventional formula for kinetic energy is in error by 0.005%. At higher speeds (all of which are possible in atoms) even larger errors occur if special relativity is not taken into account.

A fully consistent explanation of the properties of atoms, electrons and radiation would therefore need to combine electromagnetism with quantum physics and special relativity, to produce what is called a relativistic quantum theory of these properties.

The first stage in this process was completed by Paul Dirac (Figure 36) in 1928. Dirac successfully combined special relativity with the quantum model of the atom, and derived a complicated and precise formula for the energy levels of hydrogen. The differences between the predictions of his formula and the *gross* structure of the hydrogen energy levels that were known about previously show up as so-called *fine structure* in the emission lines of the hydrogen spectrum. If you were able to look closely at the lines in the hydrogen spectrum, you would see that many of them are composed of several lines very close together. Dirac's formula for the energy levels depends on the value of α_{em} and is the reason why this is known as the fine structure constant.

Dirac's work also gave a clue to how electromagnetic interactions might be modified by quantum effects. To achieve a high precision in describing tiny corrections to the quantum model of the atom as a result of relativity, Dirac was forced to postulate the

Figure 36 Paul Adrienne Maurice Dirac (1902–1984) was a British physicist who generalized the theory of quantum physics to incorporate special relativity. One of the results of his theory was that it predicted the existence of an antiparticle to the electron, which is now known as the positron.

existence of a new particle, with the same mass as the electron, but with positive charge. As you saw earlier in Chapter 2, we call this particle, e$^+$, the positron, or antielectron. Now, as you have also seen earlier, in the process of pair creation, high-energy photons can create electron–positron pairs, thereby producing new particles from purely electromagnetic energy. The mass energy of an electron or positron is about 500 keV, so to create an electron–positron pair requires about 1000 keV or 1 MeV of energy.

○ What are the typical separations between energy levels in hydrogen atoms? What is the typical energy of a photon emitted or absorbed by hydrogen atoms?

○ Energy levels in hydrogen atoms are typically separated by only a few electronvolts. Consequently, the photons emitted or absorbed by hydrogen atoms also have energies of only a few electronvolts.

Pair creation therefore requires photon energies that are about a million times greater than the energies of a few electronvolts that are involved in the energy levels of the hydrogen atom or photons of visible light! So, at first sight, one might not need to bother about them in atomic physics. After all, the idea of energy conservation is basic to physics. Why should one need to bother about the creation of positrons, when none ever emerge from atoms, apart from the comparatively rare unstable nuclei that undergo beta-decay?

It turns out that one should bother: the conservation of energy is something that has to work out on long time-scales; on much shorter time-scales energy accounting may be, so to speak, relaxed, provided the accounts are settled in the long run. The basic rule for this had been stated by Werner Heisenberg in the 1920s:

A failure of energy conservation may be tolerated for a short time provided that the energy deficit multiplied by the time interval is less than about 4×10^{-15} eV s.

After this time the energy debt must be made good. This energy–time **uncertainty principle** embodies an important feature of the quantum world: whatever is allowed to happen will do so, sooner or later.

Try thinking of the uncertainty principle as an arrangement with your bank manager, who says you may go into the red by £100 for no more than 100 days, or by £1000 for no more than 10 days, or by £10 000 for a single day. In this scenario, anything seems to be allowed, provided the product of your debt and its duration is no more than 10^4 pound-days.

○ In this analogy, for what length of time could you borrow a million pounds?

○ The time is given by $\dfrac{10^4 \text{ pound - days}}{10^6 \text{ pounds}} = 0.01$ of a day, or about a quarter of an hour.

○ How much could you borrow for a thousand years?

○ A thousand years corresponds to 365 000 days, so the amount you could borrow is given by $\dfrac{10^4 \text{ pound - days}}{365\,000 \text{ days}} = 0.027$ pounds, or about three pence!

In physics, the general feature of the **energy–time uncertainty relation** is that you may push it to the limit: any failure of the conservation of energy may be tolerated for a certain time, provided that the limit above holds true. The terms are not generous, but they are totally flexible, within this credit limit.

The energy–time uncertainty relation led to the idea that empty space, even inside an atom, is not really empty. In informal terms, it is as if electrons and positrons were constantly appearing out of nothing, and then disappearing before bank-manager Heisenberg says their credit has run out. The space inside a hydrogen atom (and inside any other atom) is filled with transient electron–positron pairs. The (negatively charged) electrons that are created are drawn towards the (positively charged) proton at the centre of the hydrogen atom. This effectively screens the charge of the proton, as illustrated in Figure 37.

If you were to measure the electric force of attraction on an electron produced by the nucleus of a hydrogen atom (i.e. a proton) when situated relatively far away from it, you would get an answer that is quantified by the fine structure constant, $\alpha_{em} = 1/137$. This value is the effective strength of electromagnetic interactions when screening due to transient electron–positron pairs *is included*, and corresponds to the situation described by Coulomb's law (Figure 37a). However, if you were to measure the same effect at a point much closer to the nucleus, some of the transient electron–positron pairs would be farther away. Consequently, there would be *less* screening, so the effective charge of the proton would appear slightly larger, and the electric force would consequently increase (Figure 37b). In other words, at small distances, the electromagnetic interaction will appear stronger than it does at larger distances, and so be characterized by a number that is *larger* than 1/137.

These quantum effects modify the electric force in a hydrogen atom only over distances that are about 1% of the typical separation of an electron and proton. The result is to modify the energy levels by a fractional amount that is only about 1 part in a million. Yet the discovery and explanation of such tiny effects led to the development of a whole new theory, called **quantum electrodynamics** (QED). Quantum electrodynamics is the most complete theory of electric and magnetic interactions that we possess. It incorporates descriptions of the emission and absorption of photons, and is needed to understand many features of the subatomic world. In this theory, all electric and magnetic forces are envisaged as arising from the *exchange* of photons between charged particles. Electricity, magnetism, electromagnetic radiation and the behaviour of electrons in atoms are merely different

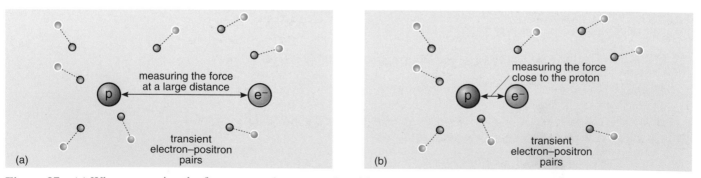

Figure 37   (a) When measuring the force on an electron produced by a proton at large distances away, some of the proton's charge is screened by transient electron–positron pairs. (b) When measuring this force much closer to the proton, there is less screening of the proton's charge, so the effective force is increased.

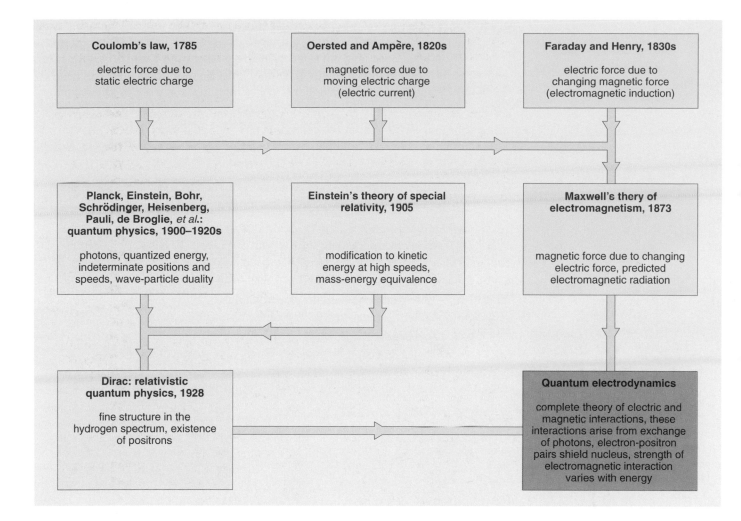

Figure 38 The development of the theory of quantum electrodynamics.

aspects of the same phenomenon. Many confirmations of this theory have now been obtained. A schematic diagram outlining the progression towards this theory is shown in Figure 38.

The final surprise of QED has already been alluded to above. It concerns how the strength of the electromagnetic interaction varies depending on the energy at which we investigate the effect. When atoms are probed in high-energy experiments, distances close to the nucleus are investigated. In these regions the strength of electromagnetic interactions is greater than the strength predicted by Coulomb's law, because shielding of the nucleus by transient electron–positron pairs is less effective. In other words, electromagnetic interactions appear *stronger* when investigated at high energies. In fact the value of α_{em} is measured to be about 1/128 (or 0.0078) at an energy of 100 GeV, compared with its lower value of 1/137 (or 0.0073) at energies of a few electronvolts. In Chapter 6 you will see that the varying strength of fundamental interactions with energy is a crucial feature that enables us to understand the conditions that prevailed in the early Universe.

5.6 Summary and questions

The electric force of attraction or repulsion between electric charges is described by Coulomb's law. This is the force that binds electrons in atoms. Like charges repel and unlike charges attract each other.

The fine structure constant, $\alpha_{em} = 1/137$, expresses the strength of electromagnetic interactions in a way that does not depend on any choice of units. It is a universal constant of nature.

In producing a theory that unified the phenomena of electric and magnetic forces, Maxwell predicted the existence of electromagnetic radiation that travels in empty space with speed $3 \times 10^8 \, \text{m s}^{-1}$, i.e. the speed of light.

By combining electromagnetism with special relativity and quantum physics, the theory of quantum electrodynamics (QED) was arrived at. This theory modifies Coulomb's law at very short distances, by taking account of the transient electron–positron pairs that can appear for short periods of time in empty space. These may be thought of as appearing and then rapidly disappearing, since a failure of energy conservation may be tolerated for a short time as long as the product of the energy deficit and time interval is less than $4 \times 10^{-15} \, \text{eV s}$.

QED predicts that the strength of electromagnetic interactions increases with increasing energy, because at the short distances probed in high-energy experiments, the shielding effect of transient electron–positron pairs is less effective.

Question 14

Summarize what was known about electric and magnetic forces before James Clerk Maxwell's work. Then summarize the key predictions made by Maxwell. ◄

Question 15

To create an electron–positron pair takes about 1 MeV of energy.

(a) Suppose the pair was created out of *nothing*, what is the maximum time for which this energy may be borrowed?

(b) How could the energy debt be repaid? ◄

Strong interactions

> Physicists are not regular fellows — and neither are poets. Anyone engaged in an activity that makes considerable demands on both the intellect and the emotions is not unlikely to be a little bit odd.
>
> Robert H. March, *Physics for poets*, 1971

There is a strong interaction that binds quarks together in nucleons (i.e. neutrons and protons). When two up quarks (u) and a down quark (d) form a proton (quark content: uud), the strong force has, largely, done its job (in much the same way that the electric force between a proton and an electron does its job, so to speak, by forming a hydrogen atom). However, there is still a residual interaction between protons and neutrons (quark content: udd), sufficient to bind them together in nuclei. This is shown in Figure 39a. The 'left-over' part of the strong interactions of quarks is similar in nature to the left-over electromagnetic interactions between atoms that are responsible for the formation of molecules and the existence of chemistry (Figure 39b).

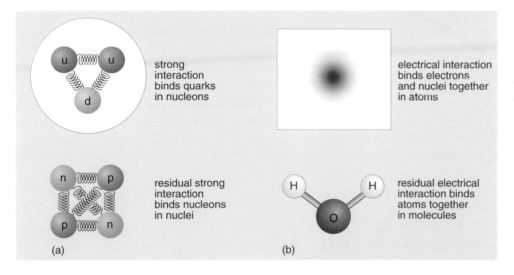

(a)

(b)

Figure 39 (a) The strong interaction binds quarks together in nucleons. A leftover interaction binds nucleons in nuclei. (b) The electromagnetic interaction binds electrons and nuclei in atoms. A left-over interaction binds atoms in molecules.

In this chapter we examine the first of the two fundamental interactions that are likely to be the least familiar to you. The strong interaction is vital for understanding how the Universe works because it is what binds quarks together inside protons and neutrons and also what allows nuclei consisting of protons and neutrons to exist. By understanding how the interaction operates, you will be able to appreciate the vital role it played in the very early Universe. Quite simply, the strong interaction enabled the fundamental particles created out of the Big Bang to begin to bind together to form the more familiar nuclei of which the present-day Universe is composed.

6.1 How strong is strong?

It is amazing just how strong the strong force between quarks is. At a separation of around 10^{-15} m — the typical size of a proton or neutron — the force of attraction between a pair of quarks is equivalent to the weight of a 10 tonne truck! As might be suggested by its name, the strong force of attraction between two up quarks is much larger than the electric force of repulsion between them. Most importantly, the strong

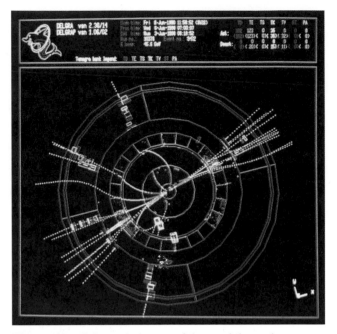

Figure 40 Schematic image of the particle tracks resulting from a collision in the Large Electron–Positron collider.

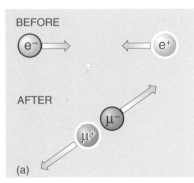

Figure 41 Two possible outcomes of an electron–positron collision: (a) a muon–antimuon pair; (b) a pair of jets of hadrons.

force between quarks does *not* get smaller at separations larger than 10^{-15} m; it stays more or less constant (with the weight of a 10 tonne truck). It is as if every quark were attached by an extremely strong elastic band to every other quark, or antiquark, that inhabits the same hadron (Figure 39a). The tension in this elastic band is the weight of a 10 tonne truck, yet it acts on a quark whose mass is 10^{30} times less than such a truck.

It is this strong force that prevents quarks from being liberated in high-energy collisions. Free quarks are *never* seen to emerge from such processes: quarks only exist confined within baryons or mesons. Consider, for example, an experiment conducted at the Large Electron–Positron (LEP) collider, at the European Laboratory for Particle Physics (CERN), near Geneva, where positrons of kinetic energy 50 GeV collide with electrons travelling in the opposite direction, with the same kinetic energy (see Figure 40). In this case, an electron and a positron may annihilate each other, producing a quark–antiquark pair, with total energy 100 GeV or 10^{11} eV. These energies are certainly impressive: 10^{11} times greater than the few electronvolts that is typical for the energy levels of the hydrogen atom and even 10^5 times greater than the combined mass-energies of the electron and positron (i.e. 1 MeV). But what can such high energies achieve, against the strong force?

In fact, 100 GeV of energy can separate a quark–antiquark pair by only about 100 times the size of a proton. That is as one might expect, since the mass energy of a proton is about 1 GeV, and therefore corresponds to an energy about 100 times less than the energy available here. The mass energy of the proton derives from the energy of quarks confined to a region of size 10^{-15} m. Putting in a hundred times more energy (100 GeV) would allow a quark to get no more than a hundred times farther away, 10^{-13} m.

So if quarks don't emerge from these collisions, what happens to the 100 GeV that is put into the collision? Energy can't be destroyed, but can only be transformed from one kind to another. In this case, the energy comes out in the form of the mass energy and kinetic energy of many hadrons.

6.2 Jets of hadrons

In the mess of debris that results from high-energy collisions between electrons and positrons, there is a tell-tale clue as to the original interaction that occurred at very short distances: it often happens that hadrons emerge as a pair of *jets* each made up of a number of hadrons. (Remember that hadrons are composite particles made of quarks and antiquarks.) Figure 41 illustrates two apparently very different outcomes from electron–positron collisions at high energies. In (a) a muon–antimuon pair is produced; in (b) a pair of jets of hadrons appears.

○ What is a muon?

○ Recall from Chapter 2 that a muon is a fundamental particle that belongs to the class known as leptons. It is like the electron, only more massive.

Figure 42 Richard Phillips Feynman (1918–1988) was one of the most celebrated and colourful US physicists. He developed his own way of describing quantum processes, using what others now refer to as Feynman diagrams, which provide a simple way of tackling calculations in quantum physics. In 1986 Feynman served on the team investigating the explosion of the Challenger Space Shuttle. In his final tour de force of science communication, he laid bare the shortcomings of the Shuttle's design to a huge television audience.

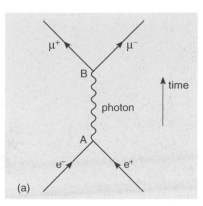

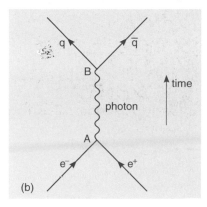

Figure 43 Feynman diagrams for the creation of:
(a) a muon–antimuon pair;
(b) a quark–antiquark pair.

In fact, the descriptions of the two basic processes in Figure 41a and b are comparable and are conveniently represented by **Feynman diagrams**. These diagrams are named in honour of Richard Feynman (Figure 42), who developed them in his study of quantum electrodynamics (QED). A Feynman diagram can be thought of as a schematic picture showing how particles interact with each other. Two or more particles may combine to form another particle, and a particle may turn into two or more other particles. Some examples are shown in Figure 43. In general, the horizontal direction in a Feynman diagram can be thought of as depicting 'space' (how far apart the particles are) and the vertical direction as 'time' (the sequence of events).

Figure 43a illustrates a Feynman diagram description, in terms of QED, of Figure 41a. It is to be read from bottom to top, with the vertical direction representing the passage of time, increasing upwards. Initially, the electron (e⁻) and positron (e⁺) are getting closer together. Their annihilation is the event labelled A. A photon is produced by the annihilation and is represented by the wavy line. In a different event, labelled B, a muon–antimuon pair is then created from the photon. From B, the muon (μ⁻) and antimuon (μ⁺) separate, as time progresses. Since both events A and B involve photons, they are both electromagnetic interactions. Notice that the lepton–antilepton pair that annihilate at A are the same flavour of lepton, and the lepton–antilepton pair that are created at B are also the same flavour. Leptons and antileptons are always created or annihilated as pairs of the *same* flavour in electromagnetic interactions.

The basic interaction that produces the pair of jets of Figure 41b is described by the Feynman diagram of Figure 43b. The difference between this and the reactions shown in Figure 41a and Figure 43a is that B is now the creation of a quark–antiquark pair (of the same flavour) from the photon which was created by the electron–positron annihilation at A. As before, both of the events A and B are electromagnetic interactions. Quarks and antiquarks too are always created or annihilated as pairs of the *same* flavour in electromagnetic interactions. The difference in outcome concerns the subsequent fate of the quark (q) and antiquark ($\overline{q}$). Unlike the muon and antimuon, they cannot separate indefinitely. Instead their kinetic energy and mass energy is converted into the kinetic energy and mass energy of many more matter and antimatter particles, including lots more quarks and antiquarks. Remember, as long as energy is conserved, any energy transformations are possible! These many quarks and antiquarks then combine to form a variety of hadrons, and these hadrons then emerge from the collision as a pair of jets. As you can probably imagine, the details of this process are much more difficult to describe than the mere separation of a muon and antimuon.

Feynman diagrams are convenient because specific mathematical expressions can be associated with each line or intersection in the diagram. This results in formulae for calculating how often a particular outcome of a reaction occurs. Different patterns correspond to different probabilities of occurrence. We shall not worry about such calculations here, but will simply use Feynman diagrams as a tool for representing different possible reactions in a graphical way. For instance, the similarity of the Feynman diagrams in Figure 43a and b indicates that the probability of producing the pair of jets is given by a calculation very much like the one for producing the muon–antimuon pair.

Now, it so happens that Figure 43a is not the whole story of what may occur in an electron–positron collision producing a muon–antimuon pair: for example, it may be that a high-energy photon is also produced. The corresponding Feynman diagram is shown in Figure 44a. As you can see there, the antimuon has lost some energy by emitting a photon. The mathematics entailed by this diagram gives a *probability* for emitting a photon, but the precise details of this calculation need not bother us. The important thing is that, in QED, the probability of a reaction occurring like that shown in Figure 44a is given by the numerical value of α_{em}, the fine structure constant. To the nearest order of magnitude α_{em} is about 0.01, so the probability of producing a photon *and* a muon–antimuon pair (Figure 44a), rather than simply a muon–antimuon pair (Figure 43a), is about 0.01 or 1%. In other words, in one out of a hundred electron-positron collision reactions, a photon and a muon-antimuon pair will be produced, whereas in 99 out of a 100 such reactions, only a muon–antimuon pair will be produced (on average). To re-state the result:

> The fine structure constant can be thought of as a measure of how often a three-branched outcome occurs as a fraction of the two-branched outcomes.

When experimenters set up detectors to find how often a muon, an antimuon, *and* a high-energy photon are produced, they find that such an outcome is indeed about a hundred times less likely than the production of merely a muon and an antimuon, just as predicted by the theory.

🔵 Bearing in mind the conclusion of Chapter 5 that the effective strength of electromagnetic interactions *increases* with energy, what do you suppose happens to the chance of getting a three-branched outcome (Figure 44a) as the collision energy is increased?

⚪ The probability is given by the value of α_{em}, and the value of α_{em} increases with increasing energy, so the chance of a three-branched outcome will also increase with increasing collision energy.

Similarly, Figure 43b is not the whole story in the production of jets of hadrons: it may happen that *three* jets are produced. The corresponding Feynman diagram for this process is shown in Figure 44b. It involves a quite new ingredient, called a **gluon**, represented by the curly line emerging from event C. Just as photons are the quanta of energy associated with electromagnetic interactions, so gluons are the

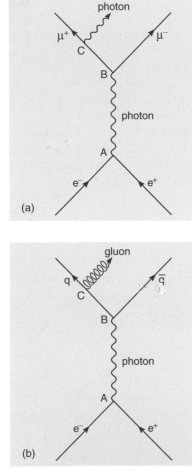

Figure 44 (a) Feynman diagram for the production of a photon, along with a muon–antimuon pair. (b) Feynman diagram for the production of a gluon, along with a quark–antiquark pair.

quanta of energy whose emission and absorption is regarded as the origin of strong interactions. Unlike photons, but like quarks and antiquarks, gluons cannot escape to large distances however.

So, a quark may emit a gluon (as shown by event C in Figure 44b) and in doing so the quark loses some energy. However, the quark still has plenty of energy left and can go on to produce a jet of hadrons, just as already described in relation to Figure 43b. A second jet of hadrons is produced by the antiquark, again as already described in relation to Figure 43b. In addition, the mass energy and kinetic energy of the gluon are quickly turned into the mass energy and kinetic energy of further pairs of quarks and antiquarks. These in turn combine with each other to form various hadrons, and the hadrons produced from the gluon then give rise to a *third* jet emerging from the process.

Notice that when a quark emits (or absorbs) a gluon, the quark does not change flavour. A similar thing is seen in electromagnetic interactions. When a charged lepton (such as an electron) emits (or absorbs) a photon, the lepton does not change flavour either.

Now, as we have just said, in QED the fine structure constant can be thought of as a measure of how likely it is that a three-branched outcome occurs, when compared with the chance of a two-branched outcome. Similarly, we can define a dimensionless estimate of the strength of the strong interaction on the same terms as in QED: it is simply the probability of observing a three-jet outcome (Figure 44b), rather than a two-jet outcome (Figure 43b). We then no longer have to refer to extraneous things, such as the weight of a truck. The experimenters find that, with an available energy of 100 GeV, the number of three-jet outcomes (Figure 44b) is about 10% of the number of two-jet outcomes (Figure 43b). So the value for this dimensionless estimate of the strength of the strong interaction, referred to as α_s, must be about 10% or 0.1.

$$\alpha_s \sim 0.1$$

The final ingredient in this story of jets is that, just like in QED, the strength of the strong interaction changes with the energy of the interaction. It turns out that the probability of three-jet outcomes, as a fraction of the two-jet outcomes, *decreases* with increasing energy.

🔵 What does this tell us about the strength α_s of strong interactions?

⚪ Since the probability of three-jet outcomes is measured by the value of α_s, the strength of strong interactions must decrease at higher energies.

So, whereas in QED the strength of electromagnetic interactions *increases* with increasing energy, the strength of strong interactions *decreases* with increasing energy.

The corresponding values for α_s measured at different energies are shown in Figure 45.

This may be a good point to step back for a moment and remind you *why* we are telling you about the details of these processes that rely on the strong interaction. Remember, our goal is to understand how the Universe works, and in particular what happened in the very early Universe, soon after the Big Bang. At those very early

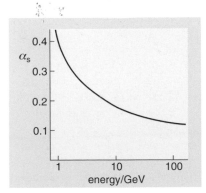

Figure 45 The decrease of α_s with energy, in the range from 1 GeV to 100 GeV. Note that the value $\alpha_s \sim 0.1$ applies at an energy of 100 GeV. At lower energies, it is considerably larger.

71

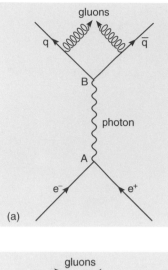

(a)

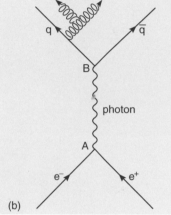

(b)

Figure 46 Two of the several ways for producing four jets of hadrons. In both processes, a high-energy collision between an electron and a positron produces a quark–antiquark pair. However, in (a), two gluons are radiated, one by a quark and one by an antiquark; in (b), a quark radiates a gluon, which then radiates a second gluon. Each of the gluons is soon converted into the mass energy and kinetic energy of further pairs of quarks and antiquarks. These in turn combine with each other to form various hadrons, and the hadrons produced from the gluons then give rise to *third* and *fourth* jets emerging from the process

times, the Universe was very hot and dense, so high-energy reactions, such as those just described, played a very important part in determining how the Universe evolved.

We now complete our summary of strong interactions by describing the theory that explains how these interactions actually work.

6.3 Quantum chromodynamics

The quantum theory of the strong interactions between quarks and gluons is called **quantum chromodynamics** (QCD). Like any quantum theory it deals, not with force directly, but with the interactions between particles and quanta, represented by an event like C in Figure 44b, where a quark emits a gluon. In quantum electrodynamics (QED) the primary interaction is of electrically charged particles with photons. In QCD there are two basic interactions: quarks (and antiquarks) interact with gluons, and gluons also interact with themselves. For example, Figure 46 gives two of the possible Feynman diagrams for producing *four* jets of hadrons. It is interactions *between* gluons that are responsible for the fact that the strength of strong interactions decreases with increasing energy.

To understand why this theory is called quantum *chromo*dynamics, you should note that 'chromo' comes from the Greek word for 'colour'. The interactions between quarks and gluons are described in terms of a new property of matter that is, rather whimsically, called **colour charge**, by analogy with conventional electric charge. Just as electromagnetic interactions result from 'forces' between electrically charged particles, so strong interactions result from 'forces' between colour charged particles. However, whereas conventional electric charge comes in only one type that can either be positive or negative, colour charge comes in *three* types, *each* of which can be 'positive' or 'negative'. These three types of colour charge are known as red, green and blue, and their opposites are antired (or the colour cyan), antigreen (or the colour magenta) and antiblue (or the colour yellow). It is important to note that colour charge has *nothing* to do with colours of light, it is merely a naming convention. By analogy with electric charge, like colour charges repel each other, and unlike colour charges attract each other.

- To what other colour charges will a particle with a red colour charge be attracted? What other colour charges will repel it?

- A particle with a red colour charge will be attracted to particles with green or blue colour charge, and also to particles with antired, antigreen or antiblue colour charge. It will be repelled by particles with red colour charge.

Each quark can have any one of the three colour charges, and each antiquark can have any one of the three anticolour charges. So in effect there are three versions of each type of quark: red up quarks, blue up quarks and green up quarks, for instance. (Remember, this is in addition to the conventional electric charge that quarks and antiquarks also carry.) Gluons each carry a combination of colour *and* anticolour charge, although they have zero electric charge. Leptons and photons *do not* have any colour charge associated with them.

This model helps to explain many phenomena, such as why the only possible hadrons are baryons (consisting of three quarks), antibaryons (consisting of three antiquarks) and mesons (consisting of one quark and one antiquark). Each of these composite particles is *colour neutral*, that is to say it has a net colour charge of zero. Any baryon

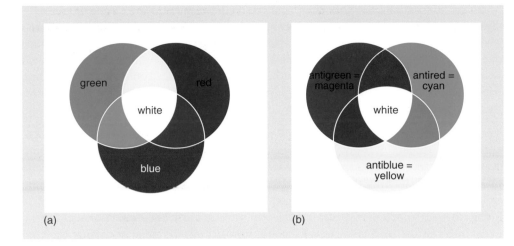

Figure 47 (a) Three colour charges combine to produce a net colour charge of zero (i.e. white). (b) Three anticolour charges combine to produce a net colour charge of zero (i.e. white).

must contain one quark with a red colour charge, one quark with a green colour charge, and one quark with a blue colour charge. By analogy with conventional colours: red + green + blue = white, a neutral colour with a net colour charge of zero, as shown in Figure 47a.

○ Can you guess what the colour charges of the three antiquarks in an antibaryon are?

○ Antibaryons must contain one antiquark with an antired colour charge, one antiquark with an antigreen colour charge, and one antiquark with an antiblue colour charge. Again this gives a net colour charge of zero, as shown in Figure 47b.

Similarly, the quark–antiquark pairs that constitute a meson must have the opposite colour charge to each other: red + antired = white for instance, which is a net colour charge of zero. Only particles with a net colour charge of zero are allowed to exist in an independent state, and this explains why single quarks and antiquarks are not seen in isolation. The locking up of quarks inside hadrons is referred to as **confinement**. Gluons do not have a net colour charge of zero either, so they too do not escape from strong interactions. Instead, gluons will decay into quark–antiquark pairs, which in turn create further hadrons.

The following points serve to compare and contrast QED and QCD.

1 In QED, photons interact with electrically charged particles and their antiparticles, but *not* directly with other photons; in QCD gluons interact with quarks and antiquarks, and *also* directly with other gluons, since all of these particles possess colour charge.

2 Photons and leptons escape from QED processes; gluons and quarks do *not* escape from QCD processes. Instead, they give rise to jets of hadrons (composite particles made of quarks) which do escape. The confinement of quarks inside hadrons results from the fact that only particles with a net colour charge of zero can exist in isolation.

3 In QED, transient electron–positron pairs cause the effective size of α_{em} to *increase* at the short distances that are probed in high-energy experiments; in QCD the interactions between gluons cause α_s to *decrease* at higher energies.

The great success of QED and QCD was to recognize that you can't have one of these differences without the other two. The self-interaction of gluons is responsible for the weakening of the strong force at higher energies, and also for confinement of quarks and gluons. Correspondingly, the fact that photons do not interact directly with other photons is related to the increasing strength of electromagnetism at higher energies, and accounts for the fact that electrons and photons emerge from atoms, in exchange for modest amounts of energy.

Thus, when we compare the strengths of electromagnetic and strong interactions, we should take account of the energy scales that are involved, and hence the associated scales of distance, bearing in mind that higher energies probe shorter distances. Even at an energy of 100 GeV though, α_{em} is still ten times smaller than the corresponding α_s of the strong interaction. But who knows what will happen at energies vastly higher than those achieved at the best laboratories on Earth? To make sense of the early Universe we need to know the answer. Fortunately, the theories predict their own fates. If no new phenomenon intervenes, the strength of the QED interaction is condemned to increase with increasing energy, whereas that of QCD must forever decrease. It is thus possible to estimate a rough value for the energy at which the two theories would have comparable strengths. The answer is thought to be about 10^{15} GeV. This is a million million times greater than collision energies currently attainable in high-energy particle physics laboratories. Yet cosmologists envisage early epochs of the evolution of the Universe when such collision energies were possible.

6.4 Summary and questions

The strong force between quarks in hadrons at a separation of 10^{-15} m is comparable to the weight of a 10 tonne truck. It confines quarks to nucleons, which are approximately this size. The forces between nucleons are a left-over effect of this force, and are of correspondingly short range.

In the collisions of electrons and positrons, with total kinetic energy 100 GeV, a variety of outcomes is possible. Sometimes a muon–antimuon pair is created; sometimes a quark–antiquark pair is created. In the latter case, the quark and antiquark cannot escape from the collision zone; instead two jets of hadrons are observed.

In collisions between electrons and positrons, the chance of radiating a high-energy photon, along with a muon–antimuon pair, is predicted by quantum electrodynamics (QED) to be roughly equal to α_{em}, i.e. about 1%. The chance of radiating a high-energy gluon, along with a quark–antiquark pair, is predicted by quantum chromodynamics (QCD) to be roughly equal to α_s, i.e. about 10%. In the latter case, the gluon cannot escape; instead a third jet of hadrons is observed.

QCD is so called because it assigns to quarks a property known as colour charge. Each type of quark can have one of three types of colour charge, but composite particles made of quarks are all 'colour neutral'.

The crucial difference between QCD and QED is that gluons interact directly with gluons, whereas photons do not interact directly with photons. This is explained in terms of both quarks and gluons possessing colour charge. There are two important consequences: quarks and gluons are not observed in isolation, and the strength of strong interactions decreases with increasing energy. Conversely, the effective strength of QED interactions increases with increasing energy.

These trends are expected to continue, with QCD and QED interactions becoming comparable at energies that are a million million times greater than can be studied at the present time in high-energy physics laboratories. Such huge energies are believed to have occurred in the very early Universe.

Question 16

In electron–positron collisions, the probability of producing *two* high-energy photons, along with a muon–antimuon pair (i.e. a four-branched outcome) is smaller than that for producing merely a muon and an antimuon, by a factor of α_{em} squared, which is $(10^{-2} \times 10^{-2}) = 10^{-4}$. By analogy with this situation, estimate the probability for producing four jets of hadrons, relative to that for producing only two jets, when the available energy is 100 GeV. ◀ $\quad \alpha_s{}^2 = 0.1 \times 0.1 = 1\%$

Question 17

Bearing in mind what you have learned about electromagnetic interactions, strong interactions, electric charge and colour charge, complete Table 8, which compares the properties of the fundamental constituents of the world around us, in terms of their electromagnetic and strong interactions. ◀

Table 8 The properties of the fundamental particles.

Particle	Electric charge	Colour charge	Quanta with which the particle interacts
electron	−ve	—	photons
electron neutrino	0	—	—
up quark	$+\tfrac{2}{3}$	RGB	gluons, photon
down quark	$-\tfrac{1}{3}$	RGB	gluons, photon
photon	0	—	electrons etc (leptons)
gluon	0	RGB (RGB)	quarks gluons

7 Week interactions

Weak interactions

There is a theory which states that if ever anybody discovers exactly what the Universe is for and why it is here, it will instantly disappear and be replaced by something even more bizarre and inexplicable. There is another theory which states that this has already happened.

Douglas Adams, 1955–2001, *The Hitch Hiker's Guide to the Galaxy*

Weak interactions manifest themselves as reactions, or decays, in which some particles may disappear, while others appear. There is no structure that is bound by a 'weak (nuclear) force', although you will often hear such a thing referred to, along with the electromagnetic force, the gravitational force and the strong (nuclear) force. Weak interactions are vital for understanding how the Universe works, as they are responsible for most of the reactions in the very early Universe by which particles changed from one sort to another. They are therefore largely responsible for the overall mix of particles from which the current Universe is made up.

The most common example of a weak interaction is beta-decay occurring in an atomic nucleus. In fact there are three related processes, each of which is a different type of beta decay. In a **beta-minus decay**, a neutron in the nucleus transforms into a proton with the emission of an electron and an electron antineutrino. In a **beta-plus decay**, a proton in the nucleus transforms into a neutron with the emission of a positron (antielectron) and an electron neutrino. Finally, in an **electron capture** process, a proton in the nucleus captures an electron from the inner regions of the atom and transforms into a neutron with the emission of an electron neutrino. In each of these three processes therefore the nucleus involved will *change* from one type of element to another, as a result of either increasing or decreasing its proton content by one. Schematically,

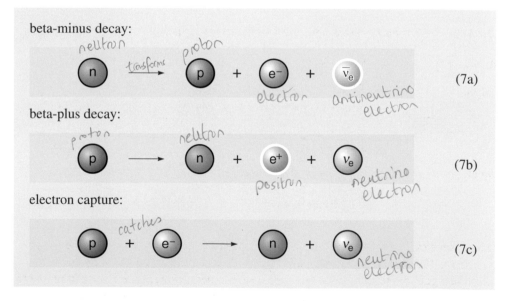

beta-minus decay: (7a)

beta-plus decay: (7b)

electron capture: (7c)

A nucleus of the unstable nitrogen isotope $^{16}_{7}\text{N}$ undergoes beta-minus decay. Write down an expression for this nuclear decay, indicating what nucleus is formed as a result.

atomic number = 7 protons   9 neutrons → 1 proton
7 electrons   1 electron
                                         1 antineutrino
                                         electron

8 electrons
8 protons
8 neutrons

$^{16}_{8}\text{O} + \bar{\nu}_e$

In beta-minus decay, a neutron turns into a proton. The mass number of the nucleus will therefore remain as 16, but the atomic number will increase from 7 to 8. The new nucleus contains 8 protons and 8 neutrons and is therefore the isotope oxygen-16. The overall reaction is therefore:

$$^{16}_{7}\text{N} \rightarrow {}^{16}_{8}\text{O} + e^- + \overline{\nu}_e$$

7.1 Comparisons between fundamental interactions

As you have seen in Chapters 5 and 6, electromagnetic interactions involve electrically charged leptons (e.g. the electron), quarks (all of which are electrically charged), and hence hadrons, made from quarks (e.g. a proton, p = uud). Strong interactions involve only particles that possess colour charge, namely quarks and gluons, as well as composite particles made from quarks. Neutrinos, which are electrically neutral leptons, are involved in neither electromagnetic interactions nor strong interactions, since they possess neither electric charge nor colour charge.

The one interaction in which neutrinos do participate is the weak interaction. The weak interactions of neutrinos from nuclear beta-decays are, as the name suggests, rather feeble. A substantial amount of the energy released in a nuclear power station escapes, innocuously, as the kinetic energy of neutrinos. The vast majority of those travelling downwards pass through the Earth without interaction. However, the probability of a neutrino interacting with matter increases with the kinetic energy of the neutrino. Beams of neutrinos with kinetic energies of the order of 100 GeV are readily obtained, as decay products, at high-energy particle accelerator laboratories. At such kinetic energies, neutrinos interact as readily with a target as do electrons. For that reason, the strength of the weak interaction is recorded, in Table 9, as being roughly the same as that of the electromagnetic interaction.

Table 9 Participants, quanta, and strengths of three interactions.

Interaction	Participants	Quanta	Strength at 100 GeV
strong	colour charged particles: u, d, c, s, t, b (and their antiparticles); gluons	gluons	$\alpha_s \sim 0.1$
electromagnetic	electrically charged particles: e^-, μ^-, τ^-; u, d, c, s, t, b (and their antiparticles)	photons	$\alpha_{em} \sim 0.01$
weak	u, d, c, s, t, b (and their antiparticles); W^+, W^-, Z^0; e^-, μ^-, τ^-, ν_e, ν_μ, ν_τ (and their antiparticles)	W^+, W^-, Z^0	$\alpha_w \sim 0.01$

The entries in Table 9 for the strong and electromagnetic interactions record what you learned in Chapters 6 and 5, respectively. The key feature of these is that the electromagnetic interactions of QED involve photons, whereas the strong interactions of QCD involve gluons. Photons interact only with particles that are electrically charged, hence neutrinos are immune to them. Gluons interact only with particles that have colour charge, hence all leptons are immune to them. What makes weak interactions so important is that they involve all six flavours of quark (u, d, c, s, t, b), all three electrically charged leptons (e^-, μ^-, τ^-), all three neutral leptons (ν_e, ν_μ, ν_τ), and all the corresponding six antiquarks and six antileptons, that you read about in Chapter 2. As you will see below, weak interactions enable quarks to change flavour into other quarks, and allow leptons to change flavour into other leptons.

7.2 W and Z bosons

Just as photons and gluons are involved in electromagnetic and strong interactions, respectively, so weak interactions involve other quanta, known as **W bosons** and **Z bosons**. In fact, there are two types of W boson, one with negative electric charge, the W⁻ boson, and one with positive electric charge, the W⁺ boson. In weak interactions, W and Z bosons interact with each other, as well as with all quarks and leptons. The Universe would be an impossibly boring place without them. To see what is involved, we will consider a very few of the many interactions that are allowed by the theory of weak interactions.

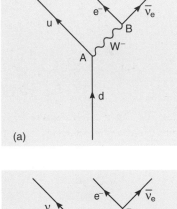

As noted above, the beta-minus decay of a nucleus occurs when a neutron turns into a proton, with the emission of an electron and an electron antineutrino. At most, a few megaelectronvolts of energy are released in this process, corresponding to the difference in mass between the original nucleus and the resultant nucleus. At the quark level, the explanation is that a down quark turns into an up quark. The process is depicted by the Feynman diagram of Figure 48a. At event A, a down quark (d) with electric charge $-1/3$ unit transforms into an up quark (u) with electric charge $+2/3$ unit. A W⁻ boson is emitted with electric charge -1 unit, thereby conserving electric charge in the process. The mass energy of the W⁻ boson is about 80 GeV, so it cannot possibly emerge from the nucleus as there are only a few megaelectronvolts of energy available. However, it can exist for a very short time, consistent with the energy–time uncertainty principle. At B it produces an electron (e⁻) and an electron antineutrino ($\overline{\nu}_e$), setting the energy accounts straight. Similarly, Figure 48b depicts the decay of a muon (μ^-), which changes at A into a muon neutrino (ν_μ), with the emission of a W⁻ boson. The W⁻ boson then decays, at B, into an electron (e⁻) and an electron antineutrino ($\overline{\nu}_e$), just as in Figure 48a.

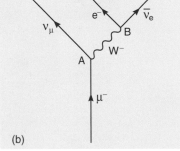

Figure 48 Feynman diagrams for weak interactions involving a W boson. (a) A beta-minus decay process, (b) the decay of a muon. Notice that a W boson is represented by a wavy line, similar to that used to represent a photon.

In both of these weak interactions, the total number of quarks minus the total number of antiquarks is the same both before and after the interaction, i.e. one quark in the beta-minus decay and zero quarks in the muon decay. The number of leptons, too is conserved. In the example of beta-minus decay, there are no leptons initially present, and after the interaction there is one lepton and one antilepton, a net result of zero again. This is the explanation for why neutrinos and antineutrinos are produced in beta decays. If they were not, then the rule of lepton conservation would be violated. Notice also that the production of a charged lepton is always accompanied by the corresponding flavour of neutrino.

⬤ Show that the total number of leptons minus antileptons remains constant both before and after the muon decay in Figure 48b.

⬤ In the example of muon decay, before the interaction there is one lepton (the muon), after the interaction there are two leptons (the electron and the muon neutrino) and one antilepton (the electron antineutrino). This gives a net result of one lepton after the interaction, so the number remains constant.

In *all* weak interactions:

- electric charge is conserved;

- the number of quarks minus the number of antiquarks is conserved;

- the number of leptons minus the number of antileptons is conserved;

- but flavour changing of either quarks or leptons is allowed, as long as these three rules are obeyed.

The third type of quantum involved in weak interactions is the Z^0 boson, which has zero electric charge. An example of the type of reaction involving the Z^0 boson is illustrated in Figure 49. Here a collision between an electron (e^-) and a positron (e^+) leads to the production of a muon neutrino (ν_μ) and a muon antineutrino ($\overline{\nu}_\mu$). Notice that there is one lepton and one antilepton both before and after the interaction.

The mass energy of a Z^0 boson is about 90 GeV. By selecting the energy of the electron and positron beams in the LEP collider to be 45 GeV each, so that the total energy of 90 GeV matched that required to create Z^0 bosons, a high rate was achieved for the production of neutrino–antineutrino pairs in the process shown in Figure 49. The experiment produced an important piece of information for understanding the early Universe: there are no more types of neutrino than the three already discovered and listed in Chapter 2: ν_e, ν_μ, and ν_τ. Had there been a fourth type of neutrino, the rate of electron–positron annihilation would have been higher than that observed, by an amount significantly greater than the sensitivity of this high-precision experiment. As noted in Chapter 1, this was good news for cosmologists, who needed this information to calculate the rate at which nuclei were formed when the Universe was a few minutes old. Knowing that there are only three types of neutrino, cosmologists are able to compute the fraction of nucleons that survived as neutrons in (mainly) helium nuclei, a few minutes after the Big Bang.

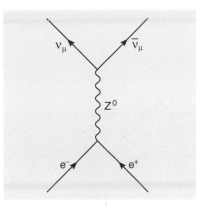

Figure 49 Feynman diagram for the production of a neutrino–antineutrino pair by an electron–positron pair, thanks to the creation and demise of a Z^0 boson.

7.3 The survival of the neutron

Apart from hydrogen, nuclei made solely of protons cannot exist. Neutrons are necessary to make nuclei stable, so the neutron is vital to our Universe. Without it there would be only a single element, hydrogen, making chemistry extremely drab, as it would be limited to a single molecule, H_2, with no one to study it.

The rules of strong interactions allow the construction of a neutron (udd) in the same manner as a proton (uud). Indeed, as we will show in Chapter 11, in the first moments of the Universe it is believed that protons and neutrons were created in *equal* numbers. Nowadays, however, the Universe as a whole contains only about one neutron for every seven protons, and the vast majority of those neutrons are locked up inside helium nuclei. Clearly then, at some stage, neutrons have 'disappeared' from the Universe. How has this happened?

The mass energy of a free neutron is about 1.3 MeV *larger* than that of a free proton. This energy difference exceeds the mass energy of an electron (which is about 500 keV or 0.5 MeV) and means that free neutrons (i.e. neutrons not bound within atomic nuclei) can undergo beta-minus decay (as shown in Figure 48a):

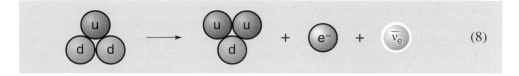

This is believed to be the mechanism by which the proportion of neutrons in the Universe decreased from one in every two hadrons soon after the Big Bang, to only around one in seven today. Once neutrons are incorporated into helium nuclei they are immune from beta-minus decay, as helium nuclei are stable.

Yet there is still a puzzle: if free neutrons can decay into protons, how did the neutrons form helium nuclei in time to avoid the fate of decay that affects them when they are free? It was indeed a question of timing. As you will see in Chapter 11, the temperature of the Universe had fallen to a value that allowed the formation of helium nuclei only a couple of minutes after the Big Bang. Since a free neutron will decay within typically about 10 minutes, there were still plenty of neutrons around at this time, and all those that had not yet decayed into protons were rapidly bound up into helium nuclei. But if the lifetime of the neutron were, say, only one second, there wouldn't have been many neutrons left to form nuclei a few minutes after the Big Bang. The vast majority of them would have long since decayed into protons. And one second is still a very long time, when compared with the lifetime of, say, an atom in an excited state, which is more like a millionth of a second. The relatively long lifetime of a free neutron is due to the fact that weak interactions (such as beta-minus decay) truly are weak, and therefore occur only rarely at low energies.

So there is a vital condition for life as we know it: weak interactions must be truly weak at low energies. If they were as strong as electromagnetic interactions at low energies, beta-minus decay processes would happen much more readily and the lifetime of a free neutron would be much shorter. As a result, the vast majority of the neutrons in the Universe would have decayed before it became possible for them to find safe havens in atomic nuclei, and there would have been no elements other than hydrogen in the Universe! Yet, at high energies, such as the 100 GeV of the LEP collider, weak interactions are comparable in strength with electromagnetic interactions, and hence only ten times weaker than strong interactions, as Table 9 records. How is this trick pulled off?

It turns out to result from the large masses of the W and Z bosons, each of which has a mass energy of around 100 GeV. In order for any weak interaction to occur, a W or Z boson must be created. But it is difficult to produce the massive W and Z bosons when the available energy is only 1 GeV. Consequently, at an energy scale of 1 GeV, where they were first investigated, weak interactions really are weak. In contrast, at an energy scale of 100 GeV, weak interactions are not so weak. At this energy, the strength of the weak interaction (α_w) is around 0.01 — the same as that of electromagnetic interactions. At this energy, W and Z bosons are easily created from the energy available. Going down a factor of one hundred in energy, from 100 GeV to 1 GeV, entails a huge decrease in the rates of weak processes. At an energy scale of 1 GeV, α_w is around 10^{-10} — a hundred million times smaller than it is at 100 GeV.

7.4 Summary and questions

Weak interactions are responsible for processes, such as beta decay, in which quarks may change flavour, and lepton–antilepton pairs may be created. They also allow leptons to change into other leptons. They involve quanta known as W bosons and Z bosons, each of which has a mass energy of around 100 GeV.

Weak interactions are weak only at low energies, where there is insufficient energy to create W and Z bosons easily. At an energy scale of 100 GeV, the strength of weak interactions is comparable with that of electromagnetic interactions, i.e. only about ten times less than that of strong interactions.

Free neutrons decay into protons after a lifetime of about 10 minutes; this is a weak interaction involving W bosons. The survival of some neutrons until helium nuclei formed in the early Universe was possible only because of the relatively long lifetime of free neutrons. This is a consequence of the weakness of weak interactions at low energies, which in turn results from the large mass of the quanta involved.

Question 18

The antiparticle of a W⁻ boson is a W⁺ boson, with the same mass, but the opposite electric charge. Draw a pair of Feynman diagrams showing how (a) beta-plus decay, and (b) the decay of an antimuon (μ^+), involve the creation and demise of a W⁺ boson. In each case check that electric charge is conserved, that the number of quarks minus the number of antiquarks is conserved, and that the number of leptons minus the number of antileptons is conserved. (*Hint*: Your diagrams should be similar to those in Figure 48, but you will have to re-label each of the lines.) ◀

Question 19

Summarize how the strengths of the three interactions that you have read about so far vary with increasing reaction energy. Be as precise as you can about their relative strengths at an energy scale of 1 GeV or lower, and at 100 GeV, using the information given in this and earlier chapters. ◀

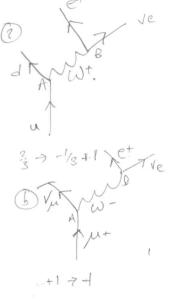

Gravitational interactions

> 'Tis like this gravity, which holds the Universe together, & none knows what it is.
>
> Ralph Waldo Emerson, 1803–1882

You may think it odd that gravitational interactions are presented last on the list of the four fundamental interactions. After all, wasn't gravity explained satisfactorily by the work of Isaac Newton in the 17th century? In fact, there are two, rather distinct additions that need to be made to Newton's description of gravity. One, involving relativity, was completed by Albert Einstein in 1915. The other, involving quantum physics, has hardly begun.

8.1 Newton's gravity

The law that describes the gravitational force of attraction was discovered by Isaac Newton (Figure 50), around 1666.

Newton's law of gravity: Two particles attract each other with a gravitational force that is proportional to the product of their masses divided by the square of their separation.

Note the close similarity with Coulomb's law for electrical force. Where Coulomb's law involves the product of two electric charges, Newton's law involves the product of two masses. Also, both forces decrease with the inverse of the square of the separation between the particles. Following Coulomb's law and the relationship between brightness and luminosity, Newton's law is therefore the third example of an inverse square law that you have met.

This is where the similarity between Coulomb's law and Newton's law ends though. It turns out that the gravitational force of attraction between a proton and an electron, separated by a distance equal to the typical size of a hydrogen atom, is about 10^{39} times *smaller* than the electric force between a proton and an electron at this same separation. As you can see, gravity is *utterly* negligible in atomic physics. In order to quantify just how small it is, we can form a dimensionless constant to describe the strength of gravitational attractions in a similar way to that in which we characterized electromagnetic interactions. Following a similar procedure to that by which we derived α_{em} in Chapter 5, the first number we calculate is the gravitational (potential) energy that exists between two electrons multiplied by their distance apart. As before, the second number is obtained by multiplying the energy of a photon by the wavelength of electromagnetic radiation corresponding to that same part of the electromagnetic spectrum. Once again, both of these numbers are therefore given as: energy × distance. Dividing the first number by the second, and multiplying by 'two pi' as before, the answer this time is about 10^{-45}!

This measure of the strength of the gravitational interaction, α_g, is a number so small that it is impossible to imagine. Comparison of the value of α_g (about 10^{-45}) with that of α_{em} (about 0.01 or 10^{-2}), shows that gravitational forces are around 43 orders of magnitude smaller (i.e. $10^{43}\times$ smaller) than electric forces, at the level of individual electrons.

Figure 50 Isaac Newton (1642–1727) was probably the greatest scientist who has ever lived. During the years 1665 and 1666, when Trinity College, Cambridge was temporarily closed due to plague, he had his most productive and creative period working at his family home in Lincolnshire. He made fundamental advances in mathematics, essentially creating the subject of calculus; he used a glass prism to demonstrate that white light is a mixture of colours; and he began to consider the possibility that gravity might be a universal phenomenon holding the Moon in its orbit around the Earth and the Earth in its orbit around the Sun.

Gravity comes into its own only when there are large aggregates of particles, feeling no other force. The strong and weak interactions of nuclei have very short ranges, so they make no contribution to the force between, say, an apple and the Earth. But why should gravitational forces dominate in this situation instead of electric forces?

- Does the gravitational force act over larger distances than the electric force?

- No, Coulomb's law and Newton's law imply that both gravitational and electric forces act over large distances with the *same* kind of inverse square law.

- Do the electric forces cancel out somehow?

- Yes, electric forces can be attractive *or* repulsive because objects can possess either positive or negative electric charge, and like charges repel whilst unlike charges attract. Gravitational forces are *always* attractive — there is no such thing as a repulsive gravitational force. The reason for this is that mass only comes in one form — 'negative mass' and 'antigravity' remain in the realm of science fiction.

So, the reason that gravity dominates the interaction between an apple and the Earth is that they are both electrically neutral, to very high accuracy. In order for the electric force of repulsion between an apple and the Earth to be similar to the gravitational force of attraction between them, only 1 atom in every 10^{20} would have to lose an electron! We owe the downwards fall of the apple to the fact that matter is electrically neutral to an accuracy far better than 1 part in 10^{20}.

8.2 General relativity

In the period between 1905 and 1915, Albert Einstein (Figure 51) wrestled with the consequences of another feature of gravity, which had been crystal clear since the time of Newton: you cannot use the motion of an apple, under gravity alone, to weigh that apple.

To understand this statement, let's start by thinking about what is meant by the words mass and weight. Many people use these words interchangeably in everyday speech, using both to refer to 'how much' of something there is. For instance, we may say that a bag of potatoes has a *weight* of 5 kg. In scientific terms however, it is more correct to say that the bag of potatoes has a *mass* of 5 kg. As we mentioned in Section 2.2, mass is a physical property that quantifies the amount of matter in a body. In contrast, **weight** is a physical property that actually tells us the strength of the gravitational force acting on a body. Weight therefore depends on the mass of a body *and* on (say) the planet on which the body is situated. If the 5 kg bag of potatoes were taken to the Moon, it would still have the same mass, but a much lower weight. This is because the strength of the gravitational force acting on the bag of potatoes on the surface of the Moon is less than that acting on the bag of potatoes on the surface of the Earth.

Now, let's return to the claim that motion under gravity cannot be used to weigh an apple. A 100 g apple and a 50 g apple have different masses and different weights. However, on Earth the two apples fall to the ground in almost the same manner, and would do so in exactly the same manner, were it not for the (frictional) force of air resistance. In a vacuum, it is impossible to determine whether a hammer weighs more or less than a feather, merely by watching them fall, because they do so at the same rate.

Figure 51   Albert Einstein (1879–1955) is widely agreed to have been the greatest physicist of the 20th century. In 1905 he published four of the most influential papers in the history of physics. Two of these outlined his special theory of relativity. Over the next few years it became clear to Einstein that an extension of his earlier work, a *general* theory of relativity, would also be a new theory of gravitation. The general theory of relativity, one of the greatest intellectual achievements of the century and a cornerstone of modern cosmology, was finally published in 1916.

The reason for this is that weight is directly proportional to mass. Doubling the mass of an object also doubles its weight, i.e. the gravitational force acting on it. The rate at which objects fall to the ground on Earth has the same value and hence tells us *nothing* about either the weight or the mass! Most of us take this fact implicitly for granted, but there is really no reason why weight and mass should necessarily be related in this manner. In case you're wondering how you can *ever* measure the mass or weight of an object, weighing machines all involve a force additional to gravity, such as that provided by the springs inside a set of bathroom scales. This enables us to measure the weight of an object by balancing two opposing forces, i.e. gravity and the spring force in a set of bathroom scales. Most such machines have a scale that indicates the mass of the object, which again implicitly assumes a direct proportionality between weight and mass, and also that you are using the weighing machine at the surface of the Earth!

To avoid the complications that the concept of weight involves, Einstein eventually chose to dispense with the idea of gravitational force entirely. Since everything falls at the same rate, he decided that it was better to think about the regions of space and time in which this motion occurs. He forgot about whether there happens to be a feather or a hammer there, since it makes no difference which is present. So he had a difficult job: to do everything that Newton had done, but without using the idea of force, and then to see if this resulted in a new prediction.

Here is not the place to describe how he went about that. Suffice it to say that he was brilliantly successful, in a mission that few had even contemplated. Einstein's **general theory of relativity** reproduced all the old results of Newton, but without even thinking about weight.

The crux of general relativity is the interaction between 'space' and the 'matter' within it. One of its basic conclusions is that objects that possess mass change the geometry of space, causing it to be 'curved'. The curvature of space then controls the movement of material objects within it. It has been said that 'matter tells space how to curve' and 'space tells matter how to move'. Gravitational effects arise as a result of the curvature of space. Taking the Solar System as an example, the Sun causes space to curve in its vicinity. The orbits of the Earth and the other planets are then a consequence of their movement through this curved space.

An analogy that is often used is the idea of placing heavy ball bearings on a taut rubber sheet, as shown in Figure 52. The rubber sheet is a two-dimensional representation of the three-dimensional space of the real Universe. The large balls

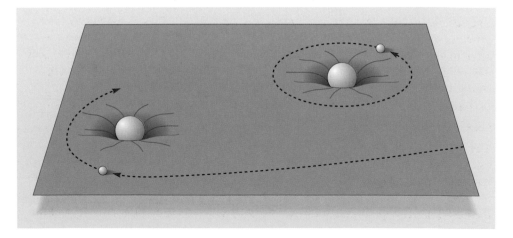

Figure 52   A two-dimensional analogy of the curvature of space caused by the presence of massive objects.

placed on the sheet represent massive objects, such as the Sun, which distort the space in their vicinity. The small ball bearings represent less massive objects, such as planets, which move in response to the curved space through which they travel.

Does that mean that Newton's idea of massive objects producing a 'force' of attraction is wrong? Well, not exactly wrong – Newton's law of gravitation is able to predict what is actually observed in a wide variety of situations. But it is only an approximation to the real world and no longer provides satisfactory answers when the masses involved become very large. Similarly, although Einstein's general relativity can cope with such situations accurately, that too fails when physicists try to unite it with the ideas of quantum physics. So general relativity too may be only an approximation to some deeper, underlying truth.

As mentioned above, Einstein did not propose general relativity in order to explain any particular experimental result. As soon as the theory had been proposed, however, various people did try to test it experimentally, and it wasn't long before experimental support for it was obtained. Some of these experimental tests are discussed below.

8.3 Curved space

The first test of general relativity was directly related to the effects of curved space, and concerned the planet Mercury. Like all the planets in orbit around the Sun, Mercury moves in an elliptical path. For a long time it had been known that the orientation of Mercury's orbit shifts slightly with time – an effect known as precession. In particular the point where Mercury is closest to the Sun advances by 0.159 degree per century, as shown in Figure 53. Ever since the mid 19th century it had been known that perturbations of Mercury's orbit by the other planets, as predicted by Newtonian gravity, could account for a shift of 0.147 degree per century, but what of the remaining 0.012 degree shift per century? As you may have guessed, general relativity was able to account for the anomalous shift in a natural way by considering the curvature of space around a massive object like the Sun.

Another consequence of the curved space in the vicinity of massive objects is that light, or any other electromagnetic radiation, passing close to a massive object will have its path bent. However, saying that gravity bends the path of light is perhaps not the correct way to look at things from the point of view of general relativity. Rather, light continues to travel in a straight line, it is just that space is curved near to a massive object, so (from sufficiently far away) its path appears to deviate.

The second test of general relativity that was available in the early 20th century concerned this prediction that the path of a beam of light would be 'bent' as it passed close to a massive object. To an observer, watching from the Earth, it would *seem* as though the light from a distant star, passing close to the Sun, has its path bent, as shown in Figure 54. For a star located along a line of sight passing close to the edge of the Sun, this would have the effect of making the apparent position of the star appear different from its true position.

The problem with a test of this kind, in the early years of the 20th century, was how can you see stars that are close to the Sun? The sky is simply too bright during the daytime. The answer is that you wait until a total solar eclipse when you *can* see stars close to Sun! So, in 1919, the British astronomer Sir Arthur Eddington sailed off to the island of Principe off the west coast of Africa and took photographs of the Sun

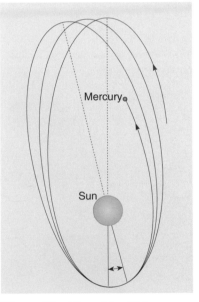

Figure 53 The orbit of Mercury around the Sun is an ellipse whose orientation shifts with time. (The double-headed arrow shows this effect, greatly exaggerated.)

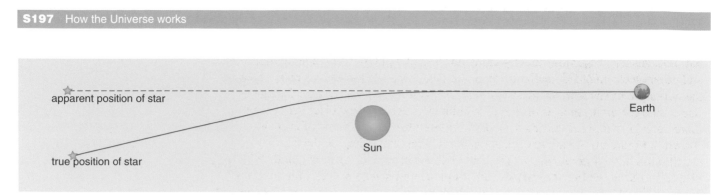

Figure 54   The bending of the path of light passing close to the Sun. This causes the apparent position of a star that lies along this line of sight to be shifted away from its true position.

during a total solar eclipse that was visible from there in May. When the relative positions of the stars were compared with their normal positions (as visible at night-time six months later or earlier) the deflections were found to agree well with the predictions of general relativity. The amount of shift is quite small — for a star exactly on the limb of the Sun, the angular shift is only about 0.0005 of a degree! Not surprisingly, the measurements made by Eddington and others around the same time had large uncertainties in the angular measurements, typically around 30%.

The situation changed with the development of **radio astronomy** during the 1960s. The first important step was that radio telescopes were constructed that could determine angular positions to an accuracy of better than 10^{-6} of a degree. The second important development was the discovery of a class of bright, point-like radio objects known as **quasars**. These are bright enough at radio wavelengths for them to be detected close to Sun without the need to wait for a total solar eclipse. A number of measurements of the deflection of radio waves from quasars as they pass close to the Sun have now been made, and they confirm the predictions of general relativity to an accuracy of better than one per cent.

A phenomenon related to that described above became apparent in 1979 when astronomers discovered what appeared to be a double quasar. The two images had similar spectra and indeed their spectra had the same redshift as each other. When one of them became brighter, so did the other one. It was soon realized that this was not two quasars, but two images of just one quasar! The situation arises as shown in Figure 55, in an effect known as **gravitational lensing**. The idea is that a massive,

Figure 55   The action of a gravitational lens.

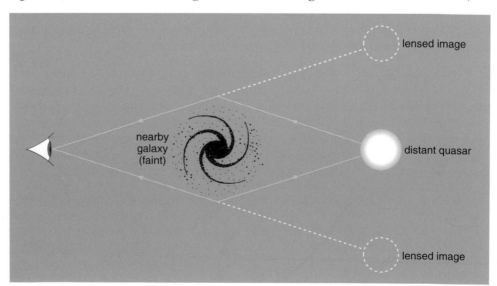

but dim, galaxy lies almost directly along our line of sight to the distant quasar. Light and other electromagnetic radiation from the quasar travels towards us and is bent by the curvature of space in the vicinity of the intervening massive galaxy. This gives rise to two (or more) images of the lensed object. Since this first discovery many more such gravitational lensing systems have been found, and some of these are shown in Figure 56. A variety of patterns is possible, depending on the mass distribution in the intervening galaxy, and just how closely the distant quasar lines up behind it. As shown in the examples, quadruple patterns and arc-like structures are possible, as well as simple paired images. Effects such as these simply don't happen in Newton's gravity.

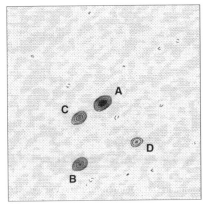

(a)

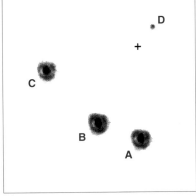

(b)

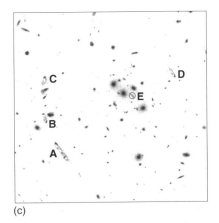

(c)

Figure 56 Some examples of gravitational lenses. (a) A radio wave image showing quadruple images of a distant quasar. The intervening, faint galaxy lies between the four images labelled A–D. This foreground object shows up on deep exposure visible light images of the same region of sky and lies at a distance of 1.8 Gpc. The multiply lensed quasar lies much farther away. (b) Another quadruple image of a distant quasar, this time in visible light in an image obtained with the Hubble Space Telescope. The lensing galaxy, whose position is marked with a cross, lies at a distance of about 1.3 Gpc. (c) In this Hubble Space Telescope image, the labels A–E identify 'arcs' that are the result of gravitational lensing by the foreground galaxies — the fuzzy blobs seen in the centre. These arcs are magnified and distorted images of a distant galaxy, lying far beyond this cluster of galaxies.

8.4 Gravitational radiation

A final confirmation of Einstein's theory of general relativity is currently on the verge of direct confirmation. It concerns what is known as **gravitational radiation**. When electrically charged particles change their speed or direction of motion they emit electromagnetic radiation. In a similar way, general relativity predicts that when massive objects undergo a change in their speed or direction of motion they will emit gravitational radiation. These gravitational waves can be thought of as ripples in the geometry of space, spreading out from their origin. They will travel at the speed of light but, in all everyday Earthbound experiences, their effects will be extremely tiny. There are objects in the Universe, however, from which astronomers will soon be able to detect gravitational waves, using detectors currently under construction.

Projects are currently underway to build gravitational wave detectors at several sites around the world, and the first of these are due for completion in the early years of this century. Gravitational radiation may be detected by the effect that it has on other objects, here on Earth. Current designs for detectors consist of two extremely long beams of laser light (hundreds of metres or several kilometres in length) orientated at right angles to each other. When a gravitational wave passes through the device it will cause very slight changes in the length of one beam relative to the other. This change in length may be measured by means of the variation produced in a pattern formed by combining the two beams. The big problem is that the distortions produced by the passage of the gravitational wave are extremely tiny. The first detectors to be built will be capable of measuring relative length changes of one part in 10^{21}. To put this in perspective, if the laser beams in the detectors stretched from the Sun to the nearest star (four light years away), the equivalent distortion in length would be about the same as the thickness of a human hair!

Even before these highly sensitive gravitational wave detectors have been completed, there is excellent evidence that gravitational radiation does exist, and astronomers can even point to a system where they know it is being produced right now. In 1974, American astronomers Joe Taylor and Russell Hulce discovered a remarkable binary star system: two neutron stars orbiting around each other once every eight hours. One of the two is also a **pulsar**, producing regular pulses of radio waves as it spins on its axis once every 59 milliseconds. This system, which became known as the binary pulsar, has proved to be an ideal test site for general relativity. It was soon discovered that the orientation of the orbit of the two neutron stars around each other shifts with time, just as the orbit of Mercury around the Sun does. But, whereas the orbit of Mercury shifts by only 0.012 degree per century as a result of general relativity, that of the binary pulsar shifts by a massive 4.23 degrees per year! The large shift is a consequence of the large mass of the two stars and the rapid speeds with which they are orbiting each other. By combining this measurement with detailed observations of the variation in radio pulsations from the pulsar around the orbit, it was possible to calculate the masses of the two neutron stars. The results were 1.42 times the mass of the Sun for the pulsing neutron star, and 1.40 times the mass of the Sun for its companion neutron star. General relativity had been used to 'weigh' a pair of neutron stars!

An even better test of general relativity was in store. As the system was monitored over several years, it was discovered that the eight hour orbital period of the binary pulsar was changing very slightly: the period becomes shorter by 75 microseconds every year. This implies that the two stars are getting closer together, and that the system is losing energy. But where is the energy going? The answer is that the system is steadily giving off gravitational radiation. Calculations showed that the rate of energy loss by gravitational radiation, as predicted by general relativity, ties in exactly with the measured changes in the orbital period of the two neutron stars. Although this gravitational radiation is predicted to be too weak to be detected by the first generation of gravitational wave detectors, there is no doubt that general relativity is being seen in action in this remarkable system.

8.5   Quantum gravity

The final remarkable feature of gravity is that no one has yet figured out a convincing way of combining quantum physics with general relativity. It is a sad irony that almost 90 years after Einstein's great work we still do not have a proper relativistic quantum theory of gravity, usually referred to simply as a theory of **quantum gravity**. Einstein made important contributions to quantum physics and he also invented relativity. If anyone deserved to discover a relativistic quantum theory of gravity, it was he. The reasons that we still haven't got one are twofold.

First, there is practically no experimental data on the interplay of gravity and quantum physics, because gravity is so weak at the level of individual particles. The second problem is a conceptual one. We have mentioned that the quantum physics of atoms involves uncertain speeds and positions for the electrons. In a quantum theory of gravity, somehow the notions of space and time themselves would have to become uncertain. In non-gravitational quantum physics one is not sure of exactly what one will measure, here and now, or there and then. In a quantum theory of gravity, one would be unsure of what here and now, or there and then, might mean!

Despite these difficulties, it is believed that quanta of gravitational energy exist. They are known as **gravitons** and have zero electric charge and zero mass. It is predicted that gravitons interact with everything: not just material bodies with mass, but also photons and gluons, which have no mass, and neutrinos, whose masses are as yet poorly known. Moreover, gravitons are predicted to interact with other gravitons. That makes photons the unique quanta that do not interact directly with themselves.

While the history of science is full of examples of experiment leading theory, as in the early days of quantum physics, or theory leading experiment, as in the case of the work of Newton, Maxwell and Einstein, it is rare to be stymied on both fronts. This has increased both the humility and determination of scientists. Recent scientific literature abounds with speculative ideas about what a quantum theory of gravity might involve, one of which will be mentioned, very briefly, in Chapter 10. The difficulty of imagining what a quantum theory of 'fuzzy' space and time might be will set a limit to how far back we can trace the history of our Universe.

8.6   Summary and questions

The gravitational force of attraction is described by Newton's law of gravity. Like Coulomb's law this is an inverse square law.

Einstein's theory of general relativity describes the interaction between space and the matter within it. When the masses become very large, this theory provides a more accurate description of gravity than does Newton's law.

Measured effects of general relativity include the precession of the orbit of the planet Mercury and gravitational lensing of quasars.

General relativity also predicts the existence of gravitational radiation. There is good evidence that such radiation is being generated by binary pulsars.

A theory of quantum gravity has yet to be formulated.

Having arrived at the conclusion that gravitational interactions do not fit so well into the pattern of description of the three other interactions, we can update Table 9 as shown in Table 10.

Table 10 Participants, quanta and strengths of four interactions.

Interaction	Participants	Quanta	Strength at 100 GeV
strong	colour charged particles	gluons	$\alpha_s \sim 0.1$
electromagnetic	electrically charged particles	photons	$\alpha_{em} \sim 0.01$
weak	quarks, leptons, W bosons, Z bosons	W bosons, Z bosons	$\alpha_w \sim 0.01$
gravitational	everything	gravitons	$\alpha_g \sim 10^{-45}$

In conclusion, we may group the descriptions of all four interactions under a variety of headings:

Quanta: Strong interactions involve gluons; electromagnetic interactions involve photons; weak interactions involve W^+, W^- and Z^0 bosons; gravitational interactions involve gravitons, though evidence for the latter is hard to come by.

Range: Electromagnetic and gravitational interactions have a large range, and both forces decrease with the inverse square of distance. Electromagnetic energy is radiated by electric charges whose speed or direction of motion changes. This energy propagates through space as an electromagnetic wave. Similarly, gravitational energy is radiated by massive objects whose speed or direction of motion changes. This energy propagates through space as a gravitational wave. Both the strong and weak interactions have a very small range, comparable with the size of individual nuclei.

Theories: Strong, electromagnetic and weak interactions are well described by relativistic quantum theories. The first to be developed was quantum electrodynamics (QED), for electromagnetic interactions. This involved combining quantum physics with special relativity and the inclusion of phenomena such as transient electron–positron pairs. Quantum chromodynamics (QCD) describes the strong interaction in a comparable way, with the key difference that the exchanged quanta, called gluons, interact with themselves, as well as with quarks. This results in the permanent confinement of quarks and gluons within hadrons, and means that quarks and gluons have never been observed in isolation. The theory of the weak interactions also involves mutually interacting quanta, W and Z bosons. Gravity awaits a 'marriage' with quantum physics.

Participants: Only quarks participate in strong interactions; quarks and charged leptons participate in electromagnetic interactions; all quarks and all leptons participate in gravitational and weak interactions.

Strength: As indicated in Table 10, the strong, electromagnetic and weak interactions have strengths that differ only by a factor of ten at energies of 100 GeV. As befits its name, the strong interaction is stronger than the other two. The weak interaction is very weak at low energies, where there is a big price to pay for exchanging its massive quanta. However, at energies around 100 GeV, the comparability of strength with electromagnetic interactions becomes apparent. Again gravity stands out on a limb, due to its almost indescribable weakness, at the level of individual particles. This makes it hard to get good data on the interplay of gravity and quantum physics. It is also hard to get good ideas about what such a theory would entail, since it must somehow incorporate a 'fuzziness' of space and time.

Question 20

It has been said that, in the theory of general relativity, matter tells space how to curve. Describe two phenomena that provide evidence for the curvature of space in the vicinity of massive objects. ◀

Question 21

Summing up the differences between Coulomb's law and modern QED theory, one might say the following: 'Coulomb's law was phrased in terms of a force between electrically charged particles. Modern QED theory describes electromagnetic interactions in terms of the exchange of photons.' Write a similar pair of sentences to describe the differences between Newton's law of gravity and what a quantum theory of gravity might involve. ◀

Four forces in the Sun

> The Sun, with all the planets revolving around it, and depending on it, can still ripen a bunch of grapes as though it had nothing else in the Universe to do.
>
> Galileo Galilei, 1564–1642

In the preceding chapters, you have seen how all processes in the Universe may be described in terms of four fundamental interactions. To consolidate your understanding of these interactions, we now look at the way in which they each operate in a relatively nearby part of the Universe — the Sun. Ultimately, it is these four interactions that are responsible for the light and other electromagnetic radiation produced by the Sun, without which life on Earth would be impossible. But here on the Earth, the only information that scientists can obtain about the Sun comes from the electromagnetic radiation and the neutrinos that it emits. A video at the end of this chapter will show you how these emissions are studied. You will see how scientists use such observations to infer what is happening deep inside the Sun, and so relate its behaviour back to the four fundamental interactions that lie at the heart of all universal processes.

9.1 Gravitational interactions in the Sun

The Sun is a ball of gas, consisting mostly of hydrogen and helium atoms, with slight traces of other, more massive elements. It has a radius of over 100 times the radius of the Earth, and over 300 000 times its mass. The large mass inside the Sun exerts a huge gravitational force on the outer layers, pulling them towards the centre. However, the Sun's radius does not appear to be changing by any great amount, so the Sun must be in an equilibrium state: the gravitational force (acting inwards) is exactly balanced by the pressure of the gas (acting outwards). It has been calculated that the pressure at the centre of the Sun is about 200 billion times the atmospheric pressure at the surface of the Earth.

When the Sun formed, it contracted under the influence of gravity from a much larger and more diffuse cloud of gas. As it did so, gravitational energy was converted into internal energy of the gas, and the result was that the temperature in the centre became very high indeed. So high in fact that nuclear fusion was initiated, and it is this process (discussed below) that maintains the high temperature and pressure in the core of the Sun today. The temperature at the centre of the Sun has been estimated at about 14 million kelvin. The high temperature implies that the particles have high kinetic energies — a few kiloelectronvolts would be a typical value.

At such a high temperature, the hydrogen and helium atoms collide with such huge kinetic energies that they are completely **ionized**. This means that the electrons are stripped away from the nuclei, giving rise to a gas of electrons and positively charged nuclei. Furthermore, the extreme pressure implies that the density at the centre of the Sun is also extremely high — about 150 times that of water — and so the electrons and nuclei are very close together. This high density of electrons and nuclei, all moving around extremely fast, provides just the conditions under which there is a high chance of a nuclear reaction taking place.

9.2 Strong and weak interactions in the Sun

Nuclear energy can provide immense amounts of power. In nuclear power stations the source of this power is nuclear fission — splitting massive nuclei apart into smaller components to release energy. In the Sun, the opposite processes — nuclear fusion — occurs, in which light nuclei become bound together into more massive ones, again with the release of energy. The process of energy release by nuclear fusion is the process that sets stars apart from other objects in the Universe. It's what defines a star to be a star.

The most abundant particles in the centre of the Sun are electrons, hydrogen nuclei and helium nuclei, and it is the hydrogen nuclei — protons — that first concern us. Under normal, Earth-bound conditions, if two protons approach close to one another they are repelled by an electric force, because both particles have a positive electric charge. However, under the conditions of extreme temperature and pressure at the centre of the Sun, the kinetic energy of some of the protons is great enough that they can approach close enough to each other for the strong interaction to bind them together before they are repelled by their similar electric charge. It should be noted, though, that the chance of any particular proton reacting with another proton is extremely rare — on average an individual proton will have to wait for more than 10 billion years before such a reaction happens! (This is just as well, or the Sun would have burnt itself out long ago.) But two protons alone do not constitute a stable nucleus. To maintain stability, one of the protons transforms into a neutron, leading to the overall reaction:

Step 1:

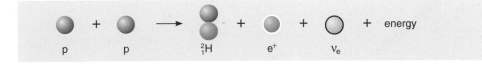

In this reaction, two protons interact to produce a nucleus of deuterium, a positron and an electron neutrino. The nucleus of deuterium is simply a proton and a neutron bound together. The net effect is that one of the original protons has been converted into a neutron, with the emission of a positron and a neutrino. It is these two particles that carry away most of the energy released by the reaction, as kinetic energy. This is identical with the process of beta-plus decay mentioned earlier. As you saw there, at a deeper level this process may be understood as the conversion of an up quark into a down quark, since a proton has the quark composition (uud), and a neutron has the composition (udd).

◔ How may this process be understood in terms of the transfer of a W boson?

◔ As you saw in Figure 80 in the answer to Question 18, an up quark can transform into a down quark with the emission of a W^+ boson. The W^+ boson then decays into a positron and an electron neutrino.

The positron that is produced will rapidly annihilate with one of the electrons that are present. This is an electromagnetic interaction leading to gamma-rays as follows:

Because Step 1 involves W bosons, it depends on the weak interaction. Without this, the whole process of energy release in the Sun could not even begin. So Step 1 involves the strong interaction *and* the weak interaction *and* the electromagnetic interaction; the strong interaction binds the two protons together, the weak interaction is responsible for conversion of a proton into a neutron, and the electromagnetic interaction allows the positron to annihilate with an electron.

The deuterium nucleus created in Step 1 is then able quickly to capture another proton in a process that relies on the strong interaction again overcoming the electric force of repulsion between two positively charged particles. This reaction forms a nucleus of the light isotope of helium (helium-3), with the emission of a gamma-ray photon that carries away some energy:

Step 2:

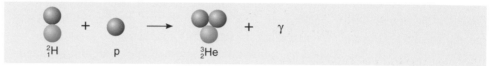

At this stage, two possibilities arise. The helium-3 nucleus can combine either with another helium-3 nucleus, or with a helium-4 nucleus. (The material from which the Sun formed contained roughly one helium-4 nucleus for every 12 hydrogen nuclei.) However, about 86% of the helium-3 nuclei follow the first route and in this case the reaction may be represented by:

Step 3:

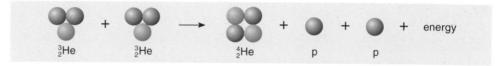

In this reaction, which relies on the strong interaction yet again, two helium-3 nuclei combine to form a helium-4 nucleus, with the emission of a pair of protons. The protons carry away most of the energy released in this reaction as kinetic energy.

The second route, in which nuclei of helium-3 and helium-4 interact, involves the creation and demise of nuclei of lithium, beryllium and boron along the way. The net result of the process, as far as nuclei are concerned, is that two helium-4 nuclei are formed at the end of it — the one that went in, as it were, and a newly created one. As a result of weak interactions, electron neutrinos are also produced in these other reactions, with energies that are different from those of the neutrinos produced in Step 1. The detection of these neutrinos with a range of energies provides one of the most sensitive tracers of the processes deep within the Sun, as you will see in Activity 2.

⬤ What is the overall result of the process described in Steps 1 to 3 above?

◯ Three protons are required to make each helium-3 nucleus (Steps 1 and 2), and then two helium-3 nuclei are required to create a helium-4 nucleus and release two protons (Step 3). In total, six protons give rise to a nucleus of helium-4, and two protons are released, along with two positrons, two electron neutrinos, and gamma-ray photons.

Whichever route is followed, the overall process involves the conversion of four hydrogen nuclei (protons) into a single helium-4 nucleus — a sequence often referred to as the **proton–proton chain**. Let us now examine the implications of energy conservation in this process.

Worked example 4

You have already seen that the mass energy of a proton or neutron is about 1 GeV. In order to look at the energy budget in the proton–proton chain, we must use rather more accurate numbers for the mass energies of the various particles. The mass energy of a helium-4 nucleus is 3.727 GeV and for a proton it is actually 0.938 GeV. How much energy is liberated as a result of the proton–proton chain?

Answer

In the reaction chain discussed above, a mass energy of $4 \times 0.938\,\text{GeV} = 3.752\,\text{GeV}$ 'goes in' but a mass energy of only 3.727 GeV appears in the products. There is therefore an apparent mass energy loss of 0.025 GeV or 25 MeV. ◀

Where has this lost mass energy gone?

As you know, mass and energy may be converted from one into the other, and energy cannot be created or destroyed, merely transformed from one form to another (including mass). So this 'missing mass' appears as the mass of the positrons in Step 1 (equivalent to about 0.5 MeV each), as the energy of the gamma-ray in Step 2, and as the extra kinetic energy of all the products, at each stage (including the neutrinos). In fact, the energy released as a result of nuclear fusion reactions appears mostly in the kinetic energy of the reaction products. This means that the particles in the core of the Sun move faster, and faster means hotter. One effect of the nuclear fusion reactions is therefore to maintain the high temperatures in the centre of the Sun. Without this source of energy, the Sun would collapse under the influence of gravity.

Nuclear fusion reactions occur only within the central 2% of the Sun's volume. This is a region about 400 000 km in diameter that contains roughly 60% of the Sun's mass. Only here are the conditions of temperature and density high enough to overcome the mutual repulsion between protons due to their electric charge. The next stage of the story is to follow the fate of the energy that is produced in the core of the Sun, as that energy is transported to the surface.

9.3 Electromagnetic interactions in the Sun

Energy transport within the Sun occurs principally by two methods: convection and radiation. Convective energy transport refers to processes in which hotter material is physically transported to regions farther from the centre that are cooler. Radiative energy transport is the transport of energy in the form of photons from deep within the Sun. Figure 57 shows the regions of the Sun in which different processes occur, and the different zones are discussed in turn below.

The dominant process for energy transport within most of the Sun's interior is radiation. This process relies on electromagnetic interactions: the interaction between matter (chiefly electrons) and photons.

 In Chapter 3 you saw how atoms are able to emit and absorb photons. What can you recall about how these processes operate?

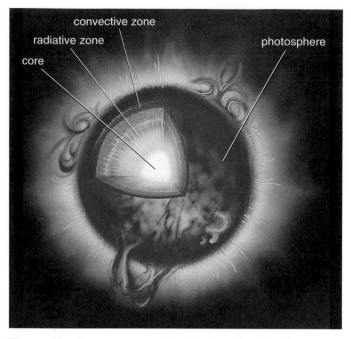

Figure 57   A cut-away model of the Sun showing the core, in which energy is liberated by nuclear fusion, the radiative zone, the convective zone, and the photosphere.

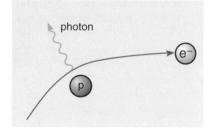

Figure 58   The process of free–free emission. An electron passing close to a nucleus will change its speed and direction of motion and in the process will emit a photon.

When an atom makes a transition from one state to another of lower energy, the energy lost by the atom is carried away by a photon in a process known as *emission*. To make atoms jump to states of higher energy, photons of the correct energies must be supplied. The energy gained by the atom is exactly equal to that supplied by the photon, in a process known as *absorption*.

Further processes will be discussed below, involving free electrons as well as electrons bound to nuclei, but all of these processes are types of electromagnetic interaction, because they involve photons. For all but the outer layers of the Sun, the temperature is such that the atoms are completely ionized — the electrons and nuclei are not bound together but are free to move about independently. The kinetic energy possessed by the electrons and nuclei comes from the energy liberated by the nuclear fusion reactions that have just been described. The process by which this kinetic energy is first converted into radiation is known as free–free emission (because the electron is 'free' both before and after emitting the photon), and is illustrated in Figure 58. Whenever a high-energy (negatively charged) electron and a (positively charged) nucleus encounter one another, they will experience an electric force of attraction. The path of the electron will change, and in the process both its speed and direction of motion will change. The energy of the electron actually has two components — kinetic energy due to its speed of motion and electrical energy associated with its position in relation to the nucleus. Initially the electron will speed up as it approaches the nucleus, but on travelling away again will slow down to a speed less than that which it initially possessed. As in any process, energy is conserved, and the net result here is that the electron loses energy, which appears in the form of a photon. Therefore, an electron moving in the vicinity of a nucleus will emit radiation.

At the temperatures that exist near to the centre of the Sun, the speeds of the particles are such that most of the photons produced by the free–free emission process will be X-ray photons with energies of a few tens of kiloelectronvolts.

How many X-ray photons of energy 25 keV could eventually be produced as a result of the 25 MeV released by each completion of the proton-proton chain?

Energy is conserved. $25\,\text{MeV}/25\,\text{keV} = 25 \times 10^6\,\text{eV}/25 \times 10^3\,\text{keV} = 1000$. Therefore a thousand X-ray photons of energy 25 keV could be produced from each completion of the proton-proton chain.

Consequently, the 25 MeV of energy liberated by *each* reaction to produce a helium-4 nucleus imparts kinetic energy to the electrons and nuclei, and then in turn provides enough energy for the production of maybe a thousand X-ray photons. Once these X-ray photons have been produced, you may think that they would simply stream out of the Sun. However, it's not quite as simple as that.

There are plenty of obstacles in the way of a photon on its way from the core to the surface of the Sun, and in fact the energy released in the centre has been estimated to take several million years to reach the surface!

The first important process by which photons are impeded on their journey to the surface is known as electron scattering. This process can be visualized as a collision between two particles. As illustrated in Figure 59, when a high-energy photon encounters a free electron, the direction of the photon will change, and so will its energy. In general, the photon will lose energy and the electron will gain energy in this process.

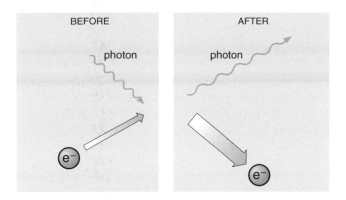

Figure 59 Scattering of photons by electrons. When a photon encounters a free electron, its direction and energy will change. In general, the photon will lose energy and the electron will gain energy in this process.

Although these interactions proceed very rapidly, the densities in the radiative zone of the Sun are so high that a photon typically travels only about 0.1 mm between each scattering event. Since each scattering changes the direction of the photon, and removes some energy, the net effect is twofold. As shown in Figure 60, it takes the photon a long time to get anywhere, and by the time it has travelled outwards from the centre by an appreciable distance, its energy has substantially decreased.

Figure 60 The so-called **random walk** of a photon travelling through the Sun. Each change in direction is the result of the photon scattering off an electron.

Another important process by which photons interact with electrons is that of *absorption*. In the radiative zone of the Sun, free electrons can absorb photons, in a process known as free–free absorption. The photon disappears and its energy is transferred directly to the electron. Unlike electrons bound in atoms, free electrons do not have energy levels, so can absorb or emit energy in any amounts. This process may be seen as the reverse of the free–free emission process described earlier.

In the outer parts of the radiative zone, temperatures, densities and pressures are all reduced somewhat. The result is that not all the nuclei are ionized, and hydrogen and helium *atoms* are present in ever increasing amounts. When photons are absorbed by atoms, they again disappear with the result that the atom as a whole gains energy. This process, which you met in Chapter 3, is often referred to as bound–bound absorption, because the electrons remain bound to the atom both before and after the event. In extreme cases, if the absorbed photon has high enough energy, an electron is ejected from the atom, carrying away some of the photon's energy, in a process known as **ionization**. Absorption processes involving bound electrons are illustrated schematically in Figure 61a and b.

An electron with sufficient energy can subsequently re-emit a photon. The process of free–free emission has already been described above. Two other ways in which a photon may be emitted are **recombination** and bound–bound emission (see Figure 61c and d). In the first of these, a free electron becomes bound to a nucleus. During this process, which is the opposite of ionization, the excess energy of the electron is carried away by a photon. The second process of photon emission is when an atom makes a transition from one quantum state to a new quantum state with a lower energy such that the atom loses energy (you met this process in Chapter 3). Each decrease in energy is accompanied by the emission of a photon, and the energy of the photon that is emitted will be equal to the energy difference between two atomic energy levels.

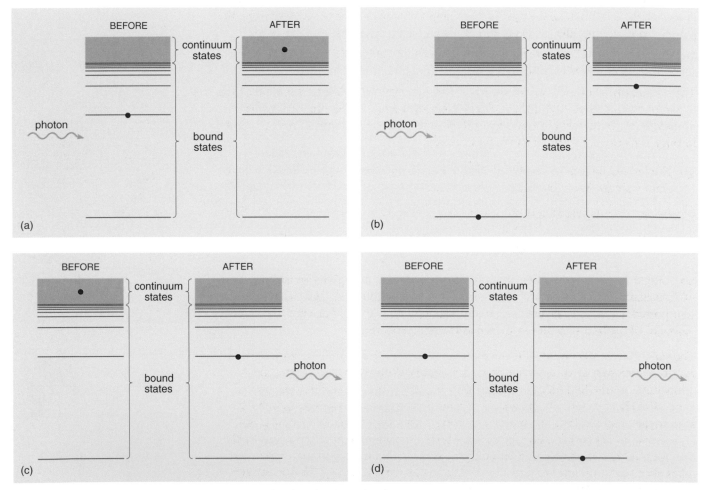

Figure 61 Absorption and emission processes that involve bound electrons. The energy levels shown are those of a hydrogen atom. When the atom has a particular value of energy, corresponding to a certain energy level, the energy level is marked with a dot. A continuum state corresponds to a separated proton and electron, so an electron in these states is described as 'free'. The processes are (a) ionization, (b) bound–bound absorption, (c) recombination, and (d) bound–bound emission.

As noted earlier, the scattering, absorption and emission processes described above mean that it takes a long time for radiation to transport energy away from the core. The zone of radiative energy transport within the Sun, throughout which these processes occur, extends from the core to within only 100 000 km of the surface (i.e. it encompasses about 86% of the radius, see Figure 57).

Beyond this point, **convection** becomes the more important mode of energy transport. Convection actually relies on the force of gravity, since convection involves regions that are 'lighter' rising above other regions that are 'heavier'. Within the convective zone of the Sun, temperatures are cool enough (a few hundred thousand degrees) for many neutral atoms to exist. Because these atoms can absorb photons, they impede the passage of radiation from below and, moving from the centre outwards, the temperature suddenly falls much more quickly. This is believed to be the trigger for convection, but the exact mechanisms operating in the Sun are still poorly understood.

Broadly speaking, as the gas in the convective zone of the Sun is heated from below, pockets of it become hotter, and so expand. These pockets are less dense than those immediately surrounding or overlying them, and so rise due to buoyancy in much the same way as a hot air balloon is able to rise. As the less dense pockets of gas rise, cooler pockets fall to take their place. On rising to the top of the convective zone, the hot gas cools again, falls to the bottom of the convective zone, and so the cycle repeats. In this way, energy is transported from the lower layers of the convective zone to the higher layers within the Sun.

The overall effect of the processes of emission, absorption, scattering and convection is that photons gradually diffuse outwards from the centre of the Sun, losing energy as they do so. In this way, the energy of the original photons is continually recycled through countless absorption and emission events.

○ How many photons of visible radiation with energy around 2.5 eV would result from a single X-ray photon of energy 25 keV?

○ Energy is not created or destroyed, merely transformed. So an energy of 25 keV is sufficient to create $\dfrac{25\ 000\ \text{eV}}{2.5\ \text{eV per photon}} = 10^4$ photons of visible radiation.

So a single X-ray photon produced in the core of the Sun may give rise to many tens of thousands of photons of visible radiation by the time the energy has been transported to the outer layers. Eventually, these photons of light emerge from the 'surface' of the Sun — a region known as the photosphere.

The photosphere sits on top of the convective region of the Sun, and is a region where radiative transport of energy once again dominates. Within the photosphere, the temperature of the Sun falls from about 6000 K, just above the convective zone, to about 4000 K at its top. The photosphere represents the region above which the Sun is transparent to radiation; no more absorption events take place above this. It is a region only about 500 km thick, but from which almost all the energy emitted by the Sun is radiated away into space. From the time it leaves the photosphere, a photon takes about eight minutes to travel to the Earth, bounce off the page in front of you, enter your eye and create an electrical response on your retina.

The light that is emitted from the solar photosphere has a continuous spectrum of radiation with a characteristic black-body shape. At higher levels in the photosphere, the lower temperatures enable the atoms to absorb photons of certain wavelengths.

Figure 62 The solar spectrum.

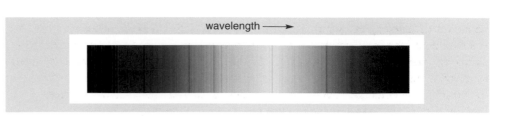
wavelength ⟶

The overall visible spectrum of the Sun, shown in Figure 62, is therefore a black-body continuum corresponding to a temperature of about 6000 K, with absorption lines superimposed on top of it. These lines of the absorption spectrum enable astronomers to determine the detailed chemical composition and physical state of the photosphere — the only part of the Sun's body that can be observed directly. For instance, it was the detection of previously unknown absorption lines in the Sun's spectrum that led to the discovery of the element helium, in the 19th century.

9.4   Solar neutrinos and helioseismology

Because the photosphere of the Sun is the *only* part of it that can be seen directly, how can astronomers possibly find out what is really happening deep inside the Sun?

It turns out that there are two ways in which information from the Sun's interior may be conveyed to its outer layers and beyond. The first involves the neutrinos that are produced as a result of the nuclear fusion reactions (Section 9.1) in the Sun's core. These **solar neutrinos** stream out of the Sun, interacting with virtually nothing along the way. In fact several million of them pass through every square centimetre of your skin every second, and the vast majority of them pass right though the Earth without even noticing it is there! So, on the one hand, because these particles come from the core of the Sun without interacting along the way, they can tell us about conditions there, but on the other hand, because they don't interact very easily it is incredibly difficult to study them to find out. In Activity 2 you will see how human ingenuity has found a way of studying solar neutrinos, and the apparent puzzle they present.

A second clue to the behaviour of the Sun is that small regions of the solar photosphere that are a few thousand kilometres in diameter are seen to regularly rise and fall with a period of about five minutes. Astronomers think that these vertical oscillations are caused by seismic waves, generated by turbulence in the convection zone, moving outwards through the Sun's atmosphere. The study of these phenomena is known as **helioseismology**, and you will find out more about it, and what it tells us about the processes deep within the Sun, in Activity 2.

> ### Activity 2   Seeing inside the Sun
> You should now watch the video 'Seeing inside the Sun'.

Since the video in Activity 2 was completed, the Sudbury Neutrino Observatory (SNO) has produced its first results and solved the **solar neutrino problem**. In April 2002, SNO reported 'direct evidence for neutrino flavour transformation'. As suggested in the video, the problem does not lie with the theories of nuclear fusion in the core of the Sun. Instead, the apparent deficit of solar neutrinos measured at the Earth is due to **flavour oscillations**. SNO has shown that the *total* number of solar neutrinos detected agrees well with the predictions of the theory, but the number of electron neutrinos is substantially less. The reason must be that some of the electron neutrinos change flavour en route from the Sun to the Earth, where they are detected as muon neutrinos and tauon neutrinos. Theories say that if neutrinos have zero mass, then they *cannot* change flavour. So, the fact that flavour changing does occur, indicates that neutrinos must possess mass.

9.5   Summary and questions

Gravity is responsible for initiating the huge temperatures, pressures and densities that exist in the core of the Sun. Such conditions are necessary in order for nuclear fusion to occur.

The strong interaction allows hydrogen nuclei to fuse together, ultimately to make helium nuclei. In the first stage of the process, the formation of a deuterium nucleus, the weak interaction is responsible for the conversion of a proton into a neutron.

The mass of a nucleus of helium-4 is somewhat less than the mass of the four hydrogen nuclei (protons) from which it is built. This 'lost' mass appears in the form of photons and increased kinetic energy of the reaction products.

The neutrinos emitted by these fusion reactions can be detected on Earth. By studying solar neutrinos, scientists have discovered that neutrinos change from one flavour to another, and so neutrinos must possess mass.

High-energy electrons undergo free–free emission processes, releasing more photons. The photons scatter from electrons, losing energy and changing direction with each interaction. Photons may be absorbed by free electrons or by atoms, and atoms or free electrons may spontaneously emit photons. The net result is that photons gradually diffuse out of the Sun.

The photons emerging from the photosphere of the Sun have a continuous spectrum that is characteristic of a black body at a temperature of about 6000 K. Superimposed on top of this are absorption lines caused by elements present within the photosphere of the Sun.

Helioseismology is the study of solar oscillations caused by seismic waves originating deep within the Sun. This technique is used to determine how the temperature and density varies throughout the Sun's interior.

Question 22

(a) Which of the three steps in the proton-proton chain depend on the weak interaction, and why?

(b) Which of the three steps depend on the strong interaction, and why? ◄

Question 23

In the process of free–free emission (Figure 58), an electron changes speed and direction when passing close to a nucleus. The electron emits a photon whose energy corresponds to its change in energy. In the process of bound–bound emission (Figure 61d), which you also met in Chapter 3, the atom makes a transition from one quantum state to another with the consequent emission of a photon.

(a) How will the allowed values of energies of the emitted photons compare in these two cases?

(b) When the results of a large number of these emission processes are examined, what will the spectra of the emitted photons look like in each case? ◀

Question 24

What happens when an electron neutrino from the Sun interacts with a deuterium nucleus in the Sudbury Neutrino Observatory detector? Explain the process at the level of (a) nuclei, (b) nucleons, (c) quarks. ◀

Unified theories

'Yes,' said Deep Thought. 'Life, the Universe, and Everything. There is an answer. But,' he added, 'I'll have to think about it.'

Douglas Adams, 1955–2001, *The Hitch Hiker's Guide to the Galaxy*

As we now know, Deep Thought's eventual answer was '42'. Might science be able to come up with something a little more satisfactory? Perhaps the answer lies in understanding the fundamental interactions that make the Universe work? The tally of these interactions was completed in Chapters 5–8. According to current reckoning there are *no more than* four fundamental interactions of all matter and radiation: strong, electromagnetic, weak and gravitational. Great interest, among physicists and cosmologists, attaches to the question: are these four interactions really so distinct, or might they be different facets of some more basic unity of nature?

The idea of unifying descriptions of force is not new: you saw in Chapter 5 that Maxwell achieved a spectacular unification of electricity, magnetism and light. Recently there has been much activity in investigating a scheme for the unification, at high energies, of weak interactions with electromagnetism. This is the subject of Section 10.1, on *electroweak unification*. The consequences will be tested by particle accelerators that are currently under construction, or at the planning stage, and some answers may be known by the time you read this.

Emboldened by this activity, some theorists have suggested a unification of the electroweak theory with QCD, the theory of the strong interaction. This is the subject of Section 10.2, on the so-called *grand unification*. Testable predictions are harder to come by, here. Perhaps the Universe itself is our best laboratory.

So as not to leave gravity out of the fold of a unified quantum theory, attempts have been made at what is called *superunification*, which is mentioned briefly in Section 10.3. Such ideas are highly speculative, but may give a clue to the nature of the very early Universe. A schematic picture for this idea of unification is shown in Figure 63, which we shall revisit over the next few sections.

Please note that Sections 10.1–10.3 are designed to give merely the flavour of enterprises that are the subject of intense current research. Unlike previous parts of the book, they contain matters on which there is no clear consensus. Nevertheless, the questions are likely to endure. Also note that the word 'unification' is used in an *active* sense. This chapter is not about armchair discussions, as to whether things are different or similar. It involves real questions about the behaviour of quarks and leptons, at very high energies, and hence it will figure in our account of the history of the Universe in Chapter 11.

A loose analogy may help. Suppose you are given three substances, at room temperature: A is a solid, B is a liquid, C is a gas. The substances are clearly different, in crucial respects. No amount of words or thought will make them into the same thing. But if you raise the temperature, so that A melts, you may discover that, as liquids, A and B have close similarities, which were unsuspected at room temperature. That might lead you to a 'unified theory of AB liquids'. Increasing the temperature further, so that both A and B evaporate, you might find strong similarities between A, B and C as gases, and hence formulate a 'unified theory of ABC gases'. It's a *little* like that with, respectively, the weak, electromagnetic, and strong interactions.

Figure 63 A schematic illustration of the unification processes that will be discussed in Chapter 10. At low energies the four fundamental interactions appear to be quite distinct, but at progressively higher energies they become unified.

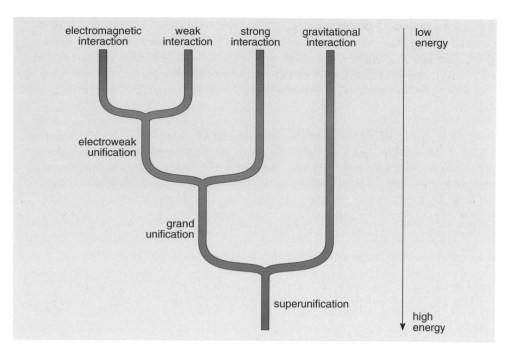

The significance for cosmology is that there was, as you've seen in Chapter 4, an early hot epoch of the Universe when weak and electromagnetic interactions may have been more unified than they now appear. There was probably an even earlier, hotter, epoch when electroweak interactions and strong interactions may have been unified. If so, radically new processes that turn quarks into leptons, and vice versa, may have been in operation, leading to a possible explanation of features of the currently observable, far cooler Universe.

10.1 Electroweak unification

You know, from Chapter 7, that the large masses of the W and Z bosons are responsible for the long half-life of the neutron, and for the very feeble interactions of low-energy neutrinos from nuclear beta decay. The similarity in strength of electromagnetic and weak interactions becomes apparent when comparing the interactions of electrons and neutrinos with kinetic energies of around 100 GeV, or greater; well below that energy, there is gross disparity.

A mechanism to explain the high-energy **electroweak unification**, and the lower-energy difference, was proposed in 1964 by a number of theorists. The name of one of them, Peter Higgs, has become attached to a new particle, the **Higgs boson**, on whose existence the proposal relies. In the mid-1990s construction began on a new particle accelerator, the Large Hadron Collider (LHC) at CERN, near Geneva, shown in Figure 2. On this machine, and its recently upgraded neighbour, the Large Electron–Positron collider mark 2 (LEP2), ride the hopes of discovering the Higgs boson, or some new surprise instead.

Just why the Higgs boson should exist is a complicated tale, but the following discussion will give you the general idea. A unified electroweak theory must be able to account for all three quanta involved in the weak interaction (W$^+$, W$^-$ and Z^0 bosons) as well as the photon that is involved in the electromagnetic interaction. The problem is that the W and Z bosons have mass and interact with each other, whereas photons are massless and do not interact with other photons. Photons cannot have mass, otherwise there would be no such thing as Coulomb's law. Massive quanta — such as the W and Z bosons — cannot produce an inverse square law of force; their effects decrease much faster with distance. The problem then is one of developing a theory that explains the existence of four quanta, three of which are different from the other one.

According to the current theory of electroweak unification, there are four so-called 'Higgs fields', one corresponding to each of the W^+, W^- and Z^0 bosons and the photon. Three of these fields 'give mass' to the W and Z bosons. The fourth field does not give mass to the photon, but will be detectable as a true particle — the Higgs boson — with a mass energy of around 1000 GeV. Therefore, at an energy scale of around 1000 GeV, the electromagnetic and weak interactions will appear truly unified and merely be different aspects of a single electroweak interaction.

⬤ Which location on Figure 63 corresponds to this energy?

◯ It is where the branches representing the electromagnetic and weak interactions join together. Write the value of this energy on Figure 63 at the appropriate place.

As you can see, the story of the Higgs boson is a somewhat tangled tale. Nevertheless, it is good science: to get a satisfactory explanation of effects at energies currently available (about 100 GeV), theorists have been led to predictions at not much higher energy (about 1000 GeV). This outline has been given because it is probable that during the lifetime of this book you will read in the newspapers one or other of the following types of headline: either (a) 'Physicists delighted: Higgs boson found'; or (b) 'Puzzle for physicists: where is the Higgs boson?'

The issue of electroweak unification is important for cosmology: what hope do we have of charting the story of the Universe back to times when the energies were enormously higher than 1000 GeV, if there is a problem in the region between 100 GeV and 1000 GeV?

10.2 Grand unification

Confirmation of the details of electroweak unification will still leave the strong and gravitational interactions out of the unified fold. Further unification of the forces of nature is an obvious theoretical challenge.

As already mentioned, the strength of the electromagnetic interactions of QED *increases*, rather slowly, with the energy transfer involved in the process. The corresponding measure of the strength of the strong interactions of QCD *decreases* with the energy transfer, again rather slowly. This raises an interesting pair of questions:

• At what energy scale might the strengths of the two interactions become equal?

• Might there be new processes at this energy scale, expressing a **grand unification** of strong and electroweak interactions, leaving only gravity out of the fold?

The answer to the first question is rather sobering: the proposed energy scale for grand unification is about 10^{11} times higher than can be achieved with even the planned new particle accelerators. As noted in Chapter 6, it is of the order of 10^{15} GeV, as compared with the energies of the order of 10^4 GeV that will be available at the Large Hadron Collider when it is completed in 2005. Such very high

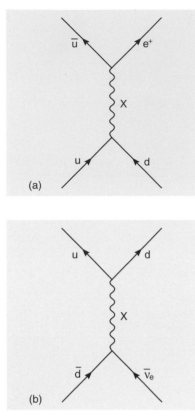

Figure 64   Some Feynman diagrams illustrating the types of new process that might occur at energies above 10^{15} GeV. (a) An up quark and a down quark react together to form an X boson, which then decays into an antiup quark and a positron. (b) An antidown quark and an electron antineutrino react together to form an X boson, which then decays into an up quark and a down quark.

energies were probably involved in the early Universe, but they will not be achieved, by human means, on Earth, for the foreseeable future. At this energy it is predicted that there is a single interaction, characterized by a single strength. Maybe Deep Thought was on the right track after all, as the strength of interactions in this *Grand Unified Theory* (GUT) is estimated to be around $\alpha_{GUT} = 1/42$ at an energy of 10^{15} GeV.

- Which location on Figure 63 corresponds to this energy?

- It is where the branches representing the electroweak and strong interactions join together. Write the value of this energy on Figure 63 at the appropriate place.

The answer to the second question 'What new processes might occur at this energy?' is rather intriguing. The expectation is that there are quite new interactions, involving bosons with mass energies of around 10^{15} GeV. Let's call such hypothetical particles **X bosons**, because we know nothing about them, directly, from experiment. The prediction is that these new interactions allow quarks to change into leptons, matter into antimatter, and vice versa in each case.

A Grand Unified Theory will have new Feynman diagrams that express these new quantum possibilities; some examples are shown in Figure 64. The reason that we have not yet seen such processes working at energies far below 10^{15} GeV is analogous to the slowness of neutron decay. Remember that weak interactions, responsible for neutron decay, involve W and Z bosons and are indeed very weak at energies far smaller than the 100 GeV that corresponds to the mass of the W and Z bosons. Processes involving X bosons would similarly be very weak at energies far smaller than the corresponding 10^{15} GeV that corresponds to the mass of an X boson, and would be incredibly slow at the energies that are currently observable (between about 100 GeV and 1000 GeV). While the behaviour of the hot early Universe would depend crucially on the processes mediated by X bosons, what we observe at lower energies hardly depends on them at all.

However, the new processes *might* show up, very rarely, at lower (i.e. achievable) energies. For example, one effect of such new processes may be that protons are not stable, but decay (eventually). The typical proton lifetime predicted by the Grand Unified Theory is around 10^{33} years, this is immensely longer than the age of the Universe, which is (only!) around 10^{10} years.

- So how might one detect proton decay, in a reasonable time, say, of one year?

- Here the intrinsically random nature of all subatomic processes helps: starting with 10^{33} protons (equivalent to a mass of over a thousand tonnes) and waiting for a few years, it might be possible to observe a few decays.

Experiments approaching this sensitivity are currently in progress, and might bear fruit within the lifetime of this book. However, even if evidence in support of grand unification emerges from searches for rare processes, such as proton decay, or (as sometimes happens in science) from less expected quarters, one step will remain in the ambitious attempt to construct a coherent 'theory of everything': the construction of a theory of quantum gravity.

10.3 Superunification: strings and branes

As already discussed, in Chapter 8, Einstein transformed the Newtonian theory of gravity as a force into a reinterpretation of space and time. His theory of general relativity entailed no quantum physics, though it profoundly modified ideas of space and time. Two of the obstacles to combining it with quantum physics have been mentioned: the difficulty of introducing ideas of uncertainty into the discussion of the properties of space and time themselves; and the lack of laboratory data against which to test such attempts.

Nevertheless, human ingenuity is proverbial. A recent aspirant to a theory that incorporates quantum gravity involves the descriptions of particles as **strings**, rather than points. Up to now, we have described the various particles (leptons, quarks, photons etc) as 'points' that can move through space as time progresses. Each particle can then be characterized by its 'position' in three-dimensional space plus one dimension of time. However, you've seen that particles have other characteristics too, such as electric charge, colour charge, and mass. All of these extra characteristics have to be put in 'by hand', as it were, to reach a complete description of the particles.

In string theory, particles are replaced by strings, which can be open (meaning they have two ends) or closed (meaning they form a loop like an elastic band). Importantly, strings can vibrate, and different modes of vibration (like different notes on a violin string) correspond to particles with different masses or charges (Figure 65). Consequently, each type of particle may be represented by a different mode of vibration. One mode of vibration makes the string look like a photon, another makes it look like a muon, yet another mode makes it look like a down quark, and so on. Crucially, there is even a mode of vibration that corresponds to a graviton.

A remarkable prediction of string theory is that space–time actually has ten dimensions. How absurd! After all, we are only aware of three dimensions of space plus one of time. Where are the other six dimensions predicted by the theory? The explanation is that the other six dimensions are curled up very small so that we don't notice them! By small we mean around 10^{-35} m, which is about 10^{21} times smaller than an atomic nucleus, so it's no wonder we haven't been aware of them until now. The reason why these extra dimensions are needed is that properties such as mass, electric charge and colour charge then correspond to movement, or vibration, of the string within these compact dimensions, just as everyday behaviour, such as speed of motion, corresponds to movement in the regular three dimensions of space plus one of time.

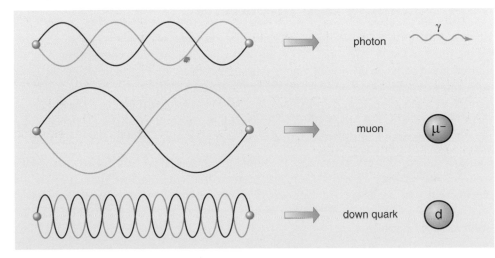

Figure 65   Different modes of vibration of strings correspond to different fundamental particles. Of course, these strings are not really like violin strings producing different notes, but the analogy is a useful one.

This is all well and good (even if a little bizarre), but physicists soon discovered not one, but *five* versions of string theory that are consistent and make sense. Some of these involved open strings, some involved closed strings, and some involved both types. If string theory really is the route to a **theory of everything**, why should there be (at least) five different varieties?

The answer to this problem came with the discovery that the five string theories are actually different aspects of a single underlying theory, now called **M-theory**. M-theory contains much more than just strings though. It contains other dimensional objects called **branes**. The word comes from 'membrane', which refers to any two-dimensional structure, like a rubber sheet for instance. In M-theory, however, branes can exist in up to *eleven* dimensions. At present, ideas such as M-theory attract some of the most fertile minds of our age, at an intellectual frontier. Whether they lead to testable predictions remains to be seen. One hope is that the difficulty of achieving **superunification**, of all four interactions, results from there being only one way of doing it, which we have not yet found.

The typical energy scale at which superunification might occur is known as the **Planck energy**, and it has a value of around 10^{19} GeV.

⬤ Which location on Figure 63 corresponds to the Planck energy?

⬤ It is where the branches representing the grand unified interaction and gravitational interaction join together. Write the value of the Planck energy on Figure 63 at the appropriate place.

It is at this scale of energy, 10^{16} times higher than the energies that have been studied on Earth, that the standard model for the history of the Universe will begin, in the next chapter. Ultimately, one might hope to derive the entire evolution of the Universe, from the Planck scale of superunification, at 10^{28} eV, through the X-boson scale of grand unification, around 10^{24} eV, down to the Higgs-boson scale of electroweak unification, now under intensive experimental investigation at 10^{12} eV on planet Earth, and from thence through the well-charted territory of Chapters 5–7, right down to the 2 eV photons of visible light that carry this message to you. Whether or not an understanding of all 28 orders of magnitude lies within the compass of the human intellect, only time will tell. In either case, it is a glorious project.

10.4 Summary and questions

Electroweak unification has been accomplished, on paper, by a theoretical device for giving mass to the W^+, W^- and Z^0 bosons, while leaving the photon massless. A consequence is the prediction of a new potentially observable particle: a Higgs boson with a mass energy of around 1000 GeV. At the time of writing, this particle is being hunted with great tenacity. If it is found, that will be a remarkable confirmation of theory; if it is ruled out, that will be a remarkable triumph of experiment. In either case, our understanding of the early Universe will increase.

Extrapolating the observed decrease of α_s and the observed increase of α_{em}, over the well-charted territory up to 100 GeV, one may predict that grand unification of electroweak and strong interactions occurs at around 10^{15} GeV. Grand unification is expected to entail X bosons that cause proton decay, at a very low rate, which may be observable on Earth.

At the Planck energy of 10^{19} GeV, a theory of quantum gravity is needed, in which the properties of space and time are as indeterminate as those of matter. Such a superunified theory is being sought.

One candidate for a superunified theory treats particles as strings, rather than points. Strings exist in ten dimensions, six of which are curled up very small. Different modes of vibration of the strings in these compact dimensions correspond to different masses, electric charge, and colour charge. So strings with different vibration modes become apparent as the various particles we know. Five different string theories have been identified, which is puzzling if they really do represent an ultimate unification.

The very latest idea for superunification is known as M- (membrane) theory. This theory incorporates all five of the previously known string theories and predicts that objects called branes exist in 11 dimensions.

Question 25

(a) Using information from this chapter and from Chapter 7, complete Table 11 to summarize information about the masses of the quanta involved in electroweak unification.

(b) What is different about photons when compared with the W and Z bosons, and what consequences does this have? ◄ *photons massless*

Table 11 Quanta involved in electroweak unification.

Quanta	Mass energy/GeV
photon	*zero* 0
W⁺ boson	*80 GeV*
W⁻ boson	*80 GeV*
Z⁰ boson	*90 GeV*
Higgs boson	*1000 GeV*

Question 26

(a) How many orders of magnitude of energy transfer have you explored in this book, from the study of atomic processes to the quest for a Higgs boson? *10^{28} 12*

(b) How many orders of magnitude are there between the highest energies we can study on Earth and those that might be entailed by grand unification? ◄ *10^{16}*

Question 27

What names are used to describe each of the new types of 'particle' predicted by:
(a) electroweak unification, (b) grand unification, (c) current ideas regarding superunification? ◄

PART III
How did the Universe get to be as it is?

In this final part of the book we pull together all the strands from the previous chapters and weave them together to tell the history of our evolving Universe from the instant of the Big Bang to the far distant future. You may find it helpful at this point to check your understanding of orders of magnitude, by reading Box 3.

Box 3   Orders of magnitude revisited

When we discuss ideas in cosmology, many quantities are not known very accurately and it is often appropriate to express them to the nearest order of magnitude, or power of ten. This can have the added bonus of making many calculations a lot simpler. We have done this already when we approximated the value of the fine structure constant as $\alpha_{em} \sim 0.01$ or 10^{-2}, for instance.

In this chapter, we shall refer to the age, temperature and energy scale of the Universe at various stages in its history. Here it is sometimes appropriate to use numbers that are *slightly* more accurate than simple orders of magnitude. To see why this is the case, think about what might be meant by the phrase 'the number mid-way between 10^5 and 10^6'. At first sight you may think the answer is 5×10^5. However, since we're dealing with orders of magnitude here, a more appropriate answer is $10^{5.5}$. But what does it mean to express ten to the power five and a half? Here is not the time or place to enter a discussion of non-whole number powers of ten, but if you have a calculator with a button on it labelled 'x^y', then key in
1 0 x^y 5 . 5 and see what answer you get.

The answer is 3×10^5 (to one significant figure). So, when dealing with orders of magnitude, the mid-point between 10^5 and 10^6 is $10^{5.5}$, which is equivalent to 3×10^5.

This is a useful concept for Chapter 11 because of a few numerical coincidences. The number of seconds in

a year is about 3×10^7 or $10^{7.5}$; one parsec is equivalent to about 3×10^{16} m or $10^{16.5}$ m; and the speed of light is about 3×10^8 m s^{-1} or $10^{8.5}$ m s^{-1}. We have said already (Section 4.1) that a temperature of 3000 K gives rise to photons whose mean energy is about 1 eV. So using the shorthand described above, you can see that an energy of 1 eV is equivalent to a temperature of $10^{3.5}$ K.

When multiplying together 'half powers of ten' such as this, the powers simply add as normal and give a whole number power, which is equivalent to saying that 3×3 is of the order of 10. This is illustrated by the following question.

● How far could a beam of light travel in one year?

○ Since distance = speed × time, the distance a beam of light could travel in one year is the speed of light multiplied by the number of seconds in one year. Namely:

$$\text{distance} = (3 \times 10^8 \,\text{m s}^{-1}) \times (3 \times 10^7 \,\text{s})$$
$$= (10^{8.5} \,\text{m s}^{-1}) \times (10^{7.5} \,\text{s})$$
$$= 10^{(8.5 + 7.5)} \,\text{m}$$
$$= 10^{16} \,\text{m}$$

As noted earlier, this distance is therefore one *light-year* and is equal to about one-third of a parsec.

The evolving Universe

11

In the beginning there was nothing at all. To the north and south of
nothingness lay regions of fire and frost.

Snorri Sturleson, 1220 AD

The cosmos is all there is, all there ever was, and all there ever will be.

Carl Sagan, 1934–1996

The two viewpoints expressed above sum up the difficulty in describing the origin of
the Universe and perhaps show that we haven't really moved very far in the 750 years
or so that separate the two statements. In this chapter, we attempt a more detailed
description than either of these. The ideas presented are the best explanation we
currently have for the reasons why the Universe has the structure, contents and
behaviour that we observe today. There are two components to study — this text and
a computer activity entitled 'A history of the Universe'.

Activity 3   A history of the Universe

In this activity we have provided you with an interactive tour of the history of
the Universe. This computer package is intended to help you to consolidate
your understanding of the processes that have occurred since the Universe was
created, in the Big Bang, up to the present day. Unlike the other computer
package, it is a resource rather than an activity in its own right. Like the text in
the rest of Chapter 11, it is presented as a story through time, with different
processes identified as being important at each epoch. It may be studied in
several ways: you may, if you wish, simply spend an hour or so stepping
through it in time, examining the processes that occurred at each point in the
history of the Universe; or you can jump in at any epoch of time and examine
the processes occurring; or you can select a particular process, and look at when
in the Universe it was important.

We suggest you start up the history of the Universe computer package now and
take a brief tour through time.

In order to get the best out of the package, you should try some of the following
tasks, using the computer package and the material in Chapter 11 to compile
your answers. There are no prescribed answers to these tasks, and most are
rather open-ended.

Task 1

A hydrogen atom consists of a proton and an electron. Explain how protons
and electrons are thought to have been created in the early Universe, and what
conditions prevailed at these times. How and when did electrons attach to
protons to form neutral hydrogen atoms?

Task 2

A star, such as the Sun, contains a significant proportion of helium nuclei. Some
of these nuclei were created within the star, others were incorporated when the
star originally formed. Explain how helium nuclei formed in each of these two
cases. Pay particular attention to the conditions necessary for these processes to
take place.

Task 3

Discuss the role of neutrinos in the Universe from the earliest times to the present day. Comment on how and when neutrinos were created, and how they are relevant to current studies of the Sun.

Task 4

Discuss the role of antimatter in the Universe from the earliest times to the present day. Why is there apparently very little antimatter in the Universe now?

Task 5

Some processes that are suggested as having occurred in the early Universe, when it was less than 10 seconds old, are rather uncertain. Describe some of the processes that may have occurred, and comment on how or why there is doubt concerning them.

Task 6

Discuss how equilibrium reactions have been important at various stages in the history of the Universe.

Task 7

Describe the particular processes that occurred in the Universe when it was (a) 10^3 (b) 10^9, and (c) 10^{15} times hotter than it is today.

11.1 Time, space, temperature and energy

The conventional view of the Universe is that, at the very instant of the Big Bang, the Universe came into being. There was no 'before' this instant since the Big Bang marked the creation of time. No location for this event can be specified since the Big Bang marked the creation of space. All that can be discussed are times after the Big Bang, and things that happen in the space created as a result of it. This is a difficult concept to visualize; but please bear with us and examine the consequences that follow. At the very end of the book, we will consider an alternative scenario to the singular Big Bang.

⬤ (a) What were the conclusions of Chapters 3 and 4 about how the separations between distant objects, and the temperature of the Universe, vary with time? (b) What does this imply about conditions in the early Universe?

◯ (a) Chapter 3 concluded that the separations between distant objects are continuously *increasing* with time. Chapter 4 concluded that the temperature of the Universe is continuously *decreasing* with time. (b) This implies that the early Universe was much *denser* and *hotter* than it is today.

The thread running through this chapter is therefore one of a Universe in which space is forever expanding, and in which the temperature is forever falling. In the early part of its history, every time the Universe increased in age by a factor of one hundred, it also cooled by a factor of ten and distances within the Universe increased by a factor of ten.

⬤ When the Universe was 1 s old, its temperature was 10^{10} K. What was the temperature of the Universe when it was (a) 100 s old, and (b) 10^4 s old?

⬤ (a) As the Universe aged from 1 s to 100 s (a factor of one hundred increase in age), so its temperature fell by a factor of ten from 10^{10} K to 10^9 K. (b) As it aged by another factor of one hundred from 100 s to 10^4 s, its temperature fell by another factor of ten from 10^9 K to 10^8 K.

The fact that the separations between objects increase only by a factor of ten for every factor of one hundred increase in the age of the Universe, actually means that the expansion rate is decreasing. For instance, two objects that were (say) 10^5 km apart when the Universe was 1 s old would be 10^6 km apart when the Universe was 100 s old, and 10^7 km apart after 10^4 s.

Worked example 5

What is the average recession speed of one of the objects referred to above, as measured from the other object, (a) when the Universe is between 1 s and 100 s old and (b) when it is between 100 s and 10^4 s old?

Answer

(a) You know that speed $= \dfrac{\text{distance}}{\text{time}}$, and that over the interval between 1 s and 100 s, the separation increases from 10^5 km to 10^6 km. Therefore the average recession speed over this interval is given by: $\dfrac{(10^6 \text{ km} - 10^5 \text{ km})}{(100 \text{ s} - 1 \text{ s})} = \dfrac{9 \times 10^5 \text{ km}}{99 \text{ s}} = 9091 \text{ km s}^{-1}$. This is of the order of 10^4 km s^{-1}.

(b) In the interval between 100 s and 10^4 s, the separation increases at an average rate of $\dfrac{(10^7 \text{ km} - 10^6 \text{ km})}{(10^4 \text{ s} - 100 \text{ s})} = \dfrac{9 \times 10^6 \text{ km}}{9900 \text{ s}} = 909 \text{ km s}^{-1}$, which is of the order of 10^3 km s^{-1}. ◀

So even though distances between objects increase by the same factor (i.e. ten) for every hundred-fold increase in time, the expansion rate of the Universe (as given by the recession speed) actually decreases with time. The expansion rate continues to decrease at later times. As mentioned in Chapter 3, this contributes to the decrease in the value of the Hubble constant with time, and is due to the gravitational attraction between all the matter in the Universe. The effect is referred to as deceleration.

The rate of cooling and expansion has changed somewhat since those early times and, as you will see later, the rate of expansion may actually have increased at some epochs. However, a consequence of the cooling and expansion is that the mean energy per particle (i.e. the energy available for any reaction to occur) is continuously reduced. This has important implications for the ways in which the four fundamental interactions manifest themselves at different epochs.

In Chapters 5 to 8 you saw that the four fundamental interactions have very different strengths and act on different types of particle. Then, in Chapter 10, you saw the clue to their unification, namely that the strengths of the interactions vary with the energy of their environment. Furthermore, at very high energies, particles can transform into different types — quarks into leptons for instance. So the fact that only quarks feel the strong interaction whilst leptons do not, is irrelevant at very high energies.

Figure 66 The unification of the four fundamental interactions as energy increases towards the bottom of the diagram. As the Universe has aged, so the mean energy of each particle has fallen, and the various interactions have become distinct from one another as the energy has fallen below the thresholds shown. The approximate ages of the Universe when each of these interactions became distinct are also shown.

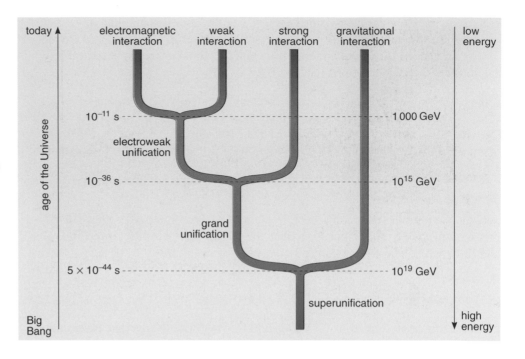

Figure 66, which is an annotated version of Figure 63, shows that at higher and higher energies, first the electromagnetic and weak interactions become unified as energies reach around 1000 GeV. Then the strong interaction becomes unified with the electroweak interaction at an energy of around 10^{15} GeV. Finally, at the very highest energies of at least 10^{19} GeV, gravity too may become unified with all the other interactions.

At the very earliest times, the Universe was extremely hot, the mean energy available per particle was extremely high, and so the unification of interactions discussed in Chapter 10 would have occurred naturally. As the Universe has cooled, the available energy has fallen, and the interactions have in turn become distinct until the current situation is reached in which four different interactions are observed. The relationship between the mean energy of a particle and the temperature of the Universe, and the time at which such energies and temperatures applied, is shown in Figure 67.

You will appreciate from Figure 67 that the rest of Chapter 11 will necessarily refer to incredibly small times after the Big Bang (notice how far along the graph 1 second appears). Many important processes took place when the Universe was significantly less than 1 s old, when the energy available for processes in the Universe was extremely high. In fact, most of the important processes were completed by the time the Universe was only a few minutes old! For each of the intervals under discussion in Sections 11.2 to 11.7 (and shown in Figure 67) the time, temperature and energy ranges are given. As you read through these sections you can imagine yourself travelling down the line of the graph in Figure 67.

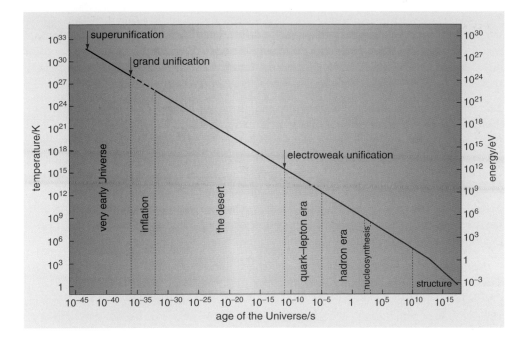

Figure 67 The mean energy per particle and temperature of the Universe at different times in its history. The divisions of this graph are described in Sections 11.2–11.7. Notice that the axes are shown on powers-of-ten scales to accommodate the vast ranges of energy, temperature and time that are necessary. You will find it useful to refer back to Figure 66 and Figure 67 as each successive stage in the history of the Universe is introduced.

11.2 The very early Universe

Time: $<10^{-36}$ s

Temperature: $>10^{28}$ K

Energy: $>3 \times 10^{15}$ GeV (i.e. $>3 \times 10^{24}$ eV)

At the very earliest times in the history of the Universe, we can only presume that a superunification of the four interactions was in operation. Unfortunately, no reliable theory of superunification is yet available, so *nothing* can be said about the contents or behaviour of the Universe in its earliest moments. Indeed, it may even be that the concept of 'time' itself had no meaning until the Universe had cooled below a certain threshold.

The first stop on the tour where anything can be said is at about 3×10^{-44} s after the Big Bang — an epoch known as the **Planck time**. By this time the mean energy per particle in the Universe had fallen to around 10^{19} GeV (the Planck energy that you met in Chapter 10). This is the energy at which the gravitational force on an individual particle has roughly the same strength as its other interactions. An idea of the typical size scale of the Universe can be gained by thinking about how far a photon of light could have travelled during this period. By the time the Universe was 3×10^{-44} s old, a beam of light travelling at 3×10^8 m s^{-1} could have travelled a distance of only about 10^{-35} m. This tiny dimension is referred to as the **Planck length**. As noted in Section 10.3, this is the sort of scale on which the hidden dimensions involved in M-theory are supposed to be curled up very small.

○ How does the Planck length compare with the typical size of an atomic nucleus?

○ In Chapter 2, the typical size for an atomic nucleus was stated as about 10^{-14} m. So the Planck length is around 10^{21} times smaller than an atomic nucleus. (It is as many times smaller than a nucleus as a nucleus is smaller than the Earth!)

As Figure 66 shows, at or around the Planck time, it is supposed that gravitational interactions became distinct from a grand unified interaction that included the three effects seen today as the electromagnetic, strong and weak interactions. In order to describe the gravitational interactions at these times a theory of quantum gravity is required. However, as you saw in Chapter 8, no such theory is yet available.

The temperature, and hence the mean energy per particle, was far higher at this time than can be recreated in particle accelerators here on Earth. Cosmologists and particle physicists can therefore only speculate on what might have occurred in the very early Universe. The best guess is that pairs of matter and antimatter particles of all types were spontaneously created out of pure energy, which can be thought of as a 'sea' of photons filling the entire Universe. With equal spontaneity, pairs of matter and antimatter particles also combined with each other again to produce photons. As you have seen earlier, the overall process of pair creation (left to right) and annihilation (right to left) can be represented as:

$$\text{photons} \rightleftharpoons \text{particle} + \text{antiparticle} \tag{9}$$

At the temperatures existing in the Universe today, reactions such as this proceed preferentially from right to left. However, at the temperatures applying in the early Universe, the reactions proceeded in both directions at the same rate, for all types of particle. A stable situation was reached in which the rates of pair creation and annihilation exactly balanced, and equal amounts of matter/antimatter and radiation were maintained.

As well as the familiar quarks and leptons, if the Grand Unified Theory discussed in Chapter 10 is correct, then this is when the particles known as X bosons would also have been in evidence. These particles are the quanta of the grand unified interaction and are suggested as a means of *converting* between quarks and leptons, or between matter and antimatter.

The next stop in time is at about 10^{-36} s after the Big Bang when the Universe had a temperature of about 10^{28} K. This temperature marks the energy at which the strong interactions became distinct from the electroweak interactions (see Figure 66).

⬤ How long after the Planck time did the strong and electroweak interactions become distinct?

⬤ Be careful here! 10^{-36} s $- 3 \times 10^{-44}$ s $= (1 \times 10^{-36}$ s$) - (0.000\,000\,03 \times 10^{-36}$ s$) = 0.999\,999\,97 \times 10^{-36}$ s. So, to all intents and purposes, the strong and electroweak interactions became distinct about 10^{-36} s after the Planck time.

It should be emphasized that there is some disagreement and uncertainty about the exact processes that occurred at this extremely early period in the history of the Universe, but the story outlined above is the best guess at what may have actually occurred. Before proceeding with the trip through time, we will pause for a moment to examine a quite remarkable event that seems to have happened just after the strong and electroweak interactions became distinct. The event has profound consequences for the nature of the Universe today.

11.3 Inflation

Time: 10^{-36} s to 10^{-32} s

Temperature: rapidly changing

Energy: rapidly changing

When talking about the Universe, there is an important distinction that our discussion has, up until now, largely ignored. First, there is the entire Universe and this may be infinite in size, as mentioned in Chapter 3. By implication, it makes no sense to put a value on the 'size' of the entire Universe, since infinity is larger than any number you care to think of. But there is also what we may call the *observable* Universe, which is that part of the Universe that it is theoretically *possible* for us to observe from Earth. We *can* calculate a value for the size of this finite region.

○ Why should there be a limit to how far we can see?

○ The speed of light is a cosmic speed limit — nothing can travel any faster. So, the only part of the Universe that is now observable is that fraction of it from which light has had time to reach us since the Universe began, about 14 billion years ago.

One might naturally expect that the radius of the currently observable Universe is therefore equal to the maximum distance that light can have travelled since the Universe began, as illustrated in Figure 68. Notice that, although light can travel from the edge of the sphere shown in Figure 68 to the centre within the age of the Universe, light *cannot* travel from one edge to the opposite edge (across the diameter of the sphere) within the age of the Universe – the Universe is simply not old enough!

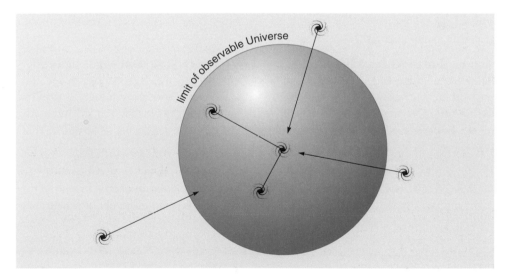

Figure 68 The size of the observable Universe. Imagine that the Earth lies at the centre of the circle (really a sphere in three dimensions), with a radius equal to the distance that light can travel since the Universe began. Then light from galaxies lying within the circle has had time to reach us, but light from galaxies lying outside the circle has not had sufficient time to reach us since the Universe began. Such galaxies are simply not observable at the current time. Furthermore, light from galaxies at one side of the circle has not had time to reach galaxies on the other side of the circle.

When trying to understand the large-scale structure of the Universe that is observed today, one of he most intriguing problems is that the Universe is so uniform. The results from the COBE satellite (Chapter 4) showed that one part of the Universe has exactly the same temperature, to an accuracy of better than one part in ten thousand, as any other part of the Universe. Furthermore, the expansion rate of the Universe in one direction is observed to be exactly the same as that in any other direction. In other words, the observable Universe today is seen to be incredibly *uniform*. At 10^{-36} s after the Big Bang, when things were far closer together than they are now, the physical conditions across the Universe must therefore have been identical, to an unimaginable level of accuracy. Yet, according to conventional physics, there has not been time for these regions of space to ever 'communicate' with one another — no light signals or any other form of energy could travel from one to the other and smooth out any irregularities.

In 1981, the American physicist Alan Guth suggested that, in the early history of the Universe at times between about 10^{-36} s and 10^{-32} s after the Big Bang, the Universe underwent a period of extremely rapid expansion, known as **inflation**. During this time, distances in the Universe expanded by an extraordinary factor — something like 10^{50} has been suggested although this could be a vast underestimate!

It is believed that inflation may be caused by the way in which the strong and electroweak interactions became distinct. The exact mechanism by which inflation occurred is not important here, but there are many consequences of this theory. The most important for the present discussion is that the region that was destined to expand to become the currently observable Universe, originated in an extremely tiny region of the pre-inflated Universe. This tiny region was far smaller than the distance a light signal could have travelled by that time and so any smoothing processes could have operated throughout the space that now constitutes the observable Universe. The problem of the uniformity of the microwave background and the uniform measured expansion then goes away.

Non-uniformities may still be out there, but they are far beyond the limits of the observable Universe — and always will be. Because we cannot ever hope to see beyond this barrier, we can have no knowledge whatsoever of events that occurred *before* inflation, since any information about such events is washed out by the rapid increase in scale. Inflation serves to hide from us any event, process or structure that was present in the Universe at the very earliest times.

If you're thinking that the inflation theory contains some pretty bizarre ideas — you're right! — but it's the most promising theory that currently exists for one of the earliest phases in the history of the Universe. We shall say no more about it here, but now pick up the story again after the Universe has completed its cosmic hiccup. The strong and electroweak interactions have now become distinct and the X bosons have therefore disappeared.

As the matter and antimatter X bosons decayed, they produced more quarks, antiquarks, leptons and antileptons — so adding to the raw materials from which the material contents of the Universe were later built. If we use X to represent a matter X boson and $\overline{X}$ to represent an antimatter X boson, the types of reaction that are believed to have occurred are:

$$X \rightleftharpoons \text{quark} + \text{quark} \tag{10a}$$

$$X \rightleftharpoons \text{antiquark} + \text{antilepton} \tag{10b}$$

$$\overline{X} \rightleftharpoons \text{quark} + \text{lepton} \tag{10c}$$

$$\overline{X} \rightleftharpoons \text{antiquark} + \text{antiquark} \tag{10d}$$

All six flavours of quark (u, d, c, s, t, b) and all six flavours of lepton (e$^-$, μ^-, τ^-, ν_e, ν_μ, ν_τ) that you met in Chapter 2 were produced at this time, along with their antiparticles. Notice, however, that matter and antimatter X bosons can each decay into *either* matter *or* antimatter particles. This will be important later on in the story.

11.4 The quark–lepton era

Time: 10^{-11} s to 10^{-5} s

Temperature: 3×10^{15} K to 3×10^{12} K

Energy: 1000 GeV to 1 GeV

During the time interval 10^{-32} s to 10^{-11} s, i.e. for the 10^{-11} seconds or so after inflation, nothing new happened in the Universe! It merely carried on expanding and cooling, but no new processes took place. The desert (as it is known) — came to an end when the Universe reached a temperature of about 3×10^{15} K, and this is where the next stage in our history begins. At this point the mean energy per particle was around 1000 GeV and the electromagnetic and weak interactions became distinct (Figure 66). As you saw in Chapter 10, the energies corresponding to this transition are becoming attainable in experiments here on Earth. So it could be argued that all particle reactions that models propose after the first 10^{-11} s of the history of the Universe are *directly* testable in Earth-based laboratories.

By 10^{-11} s after the Big Bang, the X bosons had long since decayed in reactions like those shown in Equation 10, but the temperature of the Universe was still too high for the familiar baryons (protons and neutrons) to be stable. The Universe contained all types of leptons, quarks, antileptons, and antiquarks as well as photons. In fact, there would have been approximately equal numbers of particles and antiparticles at this time — but note that word *approximately* — we shall return to the implications of this in a moment. There would also have been equal amounts of radiation (photons) and matter/antimatter (particles or antiparticles).

Now is a good time to revise your knowledge of the fundamental particles from which the Universe is built.

⦿ How do the properties of one generation of particles differ from those of each other generation?

○ As mentioned in Chapter 2, the third-generation quarks (t and b) are more massive than the second-generation quarks (c and s), which in turn are more massive than the first-generation quarks (u and d). Only upper limits to the masses of neutrinos are known, but tauons are more massive than muons, which in turn are more massive than electrons.

⦿ Which particles participate in strong interactions, weak interactions and electromagnetic interactions, respectively?

○ As summarized at the end of Chapter 8, only quarks take part in strong interactions. All quarks and leptons participate in weak interactions. All electrically charged particles experience electromagnetic interactions.

119

○ How do the charge and mass of antimatter particles differ from those of the corresponding matter particles?

○ As discussed in Chapter 2, antimatter particles have the opposite electric charge, but the same mass, as their matter counterparts. As noted in Chapter 6, antimatter quarks also have the opposite colour charge to matter quarks.

Let's now consider what the net electric charge of the Universe would have been at this time. When quarks and leptons are spontaneously produced from energy, they appear as matter–antimatter pairs with equal and opposite charge. So the net charge of the Universe remains zero, however many quarks, antiquarks, leptons and antileptons are produced in this way. But there is another way of producing leptons and quarks, namely by the decay of X bosons (Equation 10). The decays of X bosons produce:

• three quarks for every one lepton (and three antiquarks for every antilepton);

• quarks with charge +2/3 unit as often as quarks with charge −1/3 unit;

• charged leptons as often as uncharged leptons.

So, a few X bosons might decay to produce three up quarks, three down quarks, one electron and one electron neutrino, in accord with these rules.

○ What is the total electric charge of: three up quarks, three down quarks, one electron and one electron neutrino?

○ The electric charge of a single up quark is +2/3 unit, of a single down quark is −1/3 unit, of a single electron is −1 unit, and of a single electron neutrino is 0 units. So the total electric charge of this collection of particles is $(3 \times \frac{2}{3}) - (3 \times \frac{1}{3}) - 1 + 0 = 0$.

An X boson decay rate with a three to one balance between quarks and leptons therefore ensured that the net charge of the Universe remained zero.

The next stage of the story is to look at how and when the original mixture of all types of quark and lepton that were present when the Universe was 10^{-11} s old, gave rise to the Universe today, which seems to be dominated by protons, neutrons and electrons.

○ In particle accelerators, how much energy is required in order to 'create' a particle and an antiparticle of a given mass?

○ Broadly speaking, an amount of energy equivalent to (or greater than) the mass energy of the particle and antiparticle concerned needs to be supplied. For example, the mass energy of an electron is about 500 keV, so to create an electron–positron pair, at least 2×500 keV = 1 MeV of energy must be available.

In the early Universe, when the mean energy per particle was greater than the mass energy of a given particle plus antiparticle, those particles and antiparticles existed in abundance, and survived in equilibrium with radiation. When the mean energy per particle dropped below this value, annihilations became more likely than pair creations, and so the number of particles and antiparticles of a given type reduced.

Massive quarks and leptons also decay into less massive ones, and these decays became more likely as the available energy fell. You saw an example of this type of process in Figure 48b, where a muon decayed into an electron, a muon neutrino and an electron antineutrino.

● In the early Universe, what was the mean energy per particle when the following particles decayed into their less massive counterparts? (a) Top quarks with a mass energy of around 180 GeV. (b) Tauons with a mass energy of around 1.8 GeV.

○ (a) Top quarks decayed when the mean energy per particle fell below about 180 GeV. (b) Tauons decayed when the mean energy per particle fell below about 1.8 GeV.

Broadly speaking, when the temperature of the Universe fell below that at which the mean energy per particle was similar to the mass energy of the particles concerned, then the particles decayed into other less massive particles. So, by the time the Universe had cooled to a temperature of 3×10^{12} K, equivalent to a mean energy per particle of about 1 GeV, when the Universe was 10^{-5} s old, several important changes had taken place. First, many of the tauons and antitauons, muons and antimuons had decayed into their less massive lepton counterparts: electrons and positrons. Also, the temperature had fallen such that annihilation was favoured rather than pair creation for tauons and muons, so any remaining massive leptons had mutually annihilated, producing photons. The only leptons that remained in the Universe in any significant number were therefore electrons and neutrinos (with their antiparticles in approximately equal numbers).

Similarly, the massive quarks (strange, charm, top and bottom) had mostly decayed into their less massive counterparts (up and down), via a variety of transformations, some of which are shown in Figure 69. Notice that all of these decays are weak interactions, since they involve W bosons. In each case quarks change flavour with the emission of a lepton–antilepton pair.

All types of quark and antiquark also underwent mutual annihilations — with a particularly crucial result. In discussing the relative numbers of particles and antiparticles earlier, the phrase *approximately equal* was used deliberately. If the Universe had contained *exactly* equal numbers of quarks and antiquarks, then these would have all annihilated each other, leaving a Universe that contained no baryons — so no protons and neutrons — no atoms and molecules — no galaxies, stars, planets or people. Clearly that is *not* what we observe around us!

In fact the Universe now seems to consist almost entirely of matter (rather than antimatter) in the form of protons, neutrons, electrons and electron neutrinos, plus photons. And there are believed to be roughly one billion photons for every baryon (proton or neutron) in the Universe today. This implies that, just before the quark–antiquark annihilations took place, for every billion antimatter quarks there must have been *just over* a billion matter quarks. Running the Universe forward from this point, for every billion quarks and billion antiquarks that annihilated each other producing photons, a few quarks were left over to build baryons in order to make galaxies, stars, planets and people.

Why did the Universe produce this slight imbalance of matter over antimatter? Maybe it was just 'built-in' from the start, like any other constant of nature? This is rather unsatisfactory to many cosmologists and particle physicists, who prefer to believe that the imbalance arose *after* the Universe had got started. It has been suggested that the decays of X bosons into quarks and leptons *may* slightly favour the production of matter particles over antimatter particles. As you saw in Equation 10, a matter or antimatter X boson can decay into *either* matter particles or antimatter particles. So, if there is an imbalance in the rates, starting with equal numbers of matter and antimatter X bosons *will not* lead to the production of equal numbers of

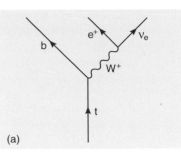

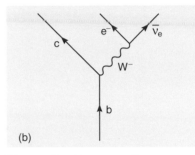

Figure 69 Feynman diagrams showing some examples of processes by which massive quarks decay into less massive quarks. In each case, electric charge, the number of quarks minus the number of antiquarks, and the number of leptons minus the number of antileptons are all conserved.

matter and antimatter quarks and leptons. Such matter–antimatter asymmetry has actually already been observed with experiments on Earth that measure the decay of particles called K mesons. Of the two possible routes for this reaction, one is favoured over the other by seven parts in a thousand. Perhaps something similar, to the tune of a few parts in a billion, occurs with X boson decays? The answer to this question is not yet known — but it's a rather important one, since without it none of us would be here to discuss the matter!

11.5 The hadron era

Time: 10^{-5} s to 100 s

Temperature: 3×10^{12} K to 10^9 K

Energy: 1 GeV to 300 keV

From the time that the temperature fell to about 3×10^{12} K, at about 10^{-5} s after the Big Bang, stable baryons (protons and neutrons) began to form from the up and down quarks that remained after the annihilation of matter and antimatter.

○ How does the mean energy per particle at 10^{-5} s compare with the mass energy of a proton or neutron?

○ Protons and neutrons have a mass energy of about 1 GeV, which is similar to the mean energy per particle in the Universe at this time.

This is why confinement of quarks became important from this time onwards. Before 10^{-5} s after the Big Bang, there had been sufficient energy available for up and down quarks to escape to distances significantly larger than the dimensions of a proton or neutron. After this time, no such escape was possible.

○ What are the quark contents of a proton and a neutron?

○ Recall from earlier that a proton is composed of two up quarks and a down quark, whereas a neutron is composed of two down quarks and an up quark.

Equal numbers of up and down quarks therefore led to an equal number of protons and neutrons emerging from this process. To recap on the contents of the Universe at this time, there were about a billion photons, electrons, positrons, neutrinos and antineutrinos for every single proton or neutron in the Universe.

○ Why had the electrons and positrons not yet mutually annihilated each other?

○ The mass energy of an electron or positron is about 500 keV, and the mean energy per particle was still much higher than the 1 MeV required to create a pair of them. So electrons and positrons were still in equilibrium with photons, undergoing both annihilation and pair creation reactions at the same rate.

As soon as baryons had formed, weak interactions took over, with protons and neutrons existing in equilibrium governed by the following processes:

$$e^+ + n \rightleftharpoons p + \bar{v}_e \tag{11a}$$

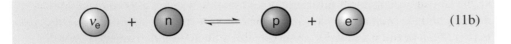

$$\nu_e \ + \ n \ \rightleftharpoons \ p \ + \ e^- \qquad \qquad (11b)$$

So neutrons converted into protons by reacting with either positrons or electron neutrinos; protons converted into neutrons by reacting with either electron antineutrinos or electrons.

- At the quark and lepton level, how may the two reactions in Equation 11 be represented?

- Bearing in mind the quark composition of a proton and a neutron, each of the reactions involve conversions between a down quark and an up quark as shown in Equations 11.5a and b:

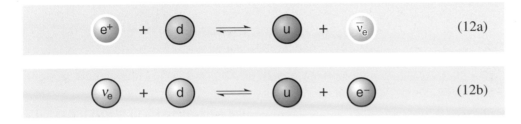

$$e^+ \ + \ d \ \rightleftharpoons \ u \ + \ \overline{\nu_e} \qquad \qquad (12a)$$

$$\nu_e \ + \ d \ \rightleftharpoons \ u \ + \ e^- \qquad \qquad (12b)$$

We can also draw Feynman diagrams to illustrate these two processes, as shown in Figure 70. Each of the two processes may be considered as arising from the *exchange* of a W boson. Furthermore, each of the parts of this figure may be read either from bottom to top, *or* from top to bottom, depending on which way the reaction in Equation 12 progresses.

- What is the change in electric charge when a positron converts into an electron antineutrino? What is the change in electric charge when a down quark converts into an up quark? How can the exchange of a W boson, as illustrated in Figure 70a, maintain conservation of electric charge in this case?

- When a positron (electric charge = +1 unit) converts into an electron antineutrino (electric charge = 0), the change in electric charge is −1 unit. When a down quark (electric charge = −1/3 unit) converts into an up quark (electric charge = +2/3 unit), the change in electric charge is +1 unit. So in Figure 70a the exchange of a W^+ boson from left to right can be thought of as carrying +1 unit of electric charge away from the positron and adding it to the down quark. Alternatively, the exchange of a W^- boson from right to left can be thought of as carrying −1 unit of electric charge away from the down quark and adding it to the positron.

With plenty of energy available, the transitions from neutron to proton and from proton to neutron proceeded at the same rate. Since there were as many neutrinos as electrons, and as many antineutrinos as positrons, the numbers of neutrons and protons in the Universe remained equal, at least initially. However, this situation did not continue. As noted in Section 7.3, the mass of a neutron is slightly higher than that of a proton. As a consequence of this, the reactions in which a proton converted into a neutron became slightly less likely to happen as the energy fell, because they required more energy than those in which a neutron converted into a proton. As the Universe cooled, this difference in the rates of the two processes became more pronounced, and protons began to outnumber neutrons for the first time.

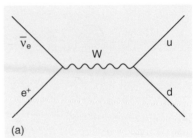

(a)

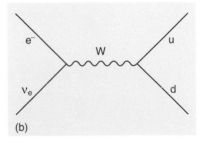

(b)

Figure 70 (a) and (b) Feynman diagrams illustrating the reactions occurring in Equations 12a and b, respectively. No arrows are shown because each of these Feynman diagrams can be read either from bottom to top (neutron to proton conversions), or from top to bottom (proton to neutron conversions). The W boson in each case may be exchanged either from left to right or from right to left. Positrons, electron neutrinos, and up quarks will emit W^+ bosons, whereas electrons, electron antineutrinos and down quarks will emit W^- bosons.

As the Universe cooled still further, another reaction became important for the neutrons and the protons: as you saw in Section 7.3, isolated neutrons decay into protons. This additional process, again governed by the weak interaction, added to the dominance of protons over neutrons in the Universe:

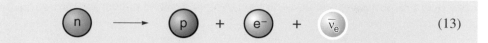

$$n \longrightarrow p + e^- + \overline{\nu}_e \qquad (13)$$

Once the Universe was 0.1 s old, the weak interactions described by the reactions in Equations 11 and 12 became too slow, and neutrinos virtually ceased to have any further interaction with the rest of the Universe — ever! The ratio of protons to neutrons continued to rise as a result of neutron decay, and was only halted (see Section 11.6) when the neutrons became bound up in atomic nuclei where they became essentially immune from decay. As you saw in Section 7.3, if the typical lifetime of the neutron (about 10 minutes) were much shorter than it in fact is, then all neutrons would have decayed into protons long before they could become confined inside nuclei.

When the Universe was about 10 s old, and the mean energy per particle was about 1 MeV, a final important event for the matter contents of the Universe occurred. The remaining primordial electrons and positrons mutually annihilated, producing yet more photons, but leaving the excess one-in-a-billion electrons to balance the charges of the primordial one-in-a-billion protons and ensure that the Universe has a net electric charge of zero.

11.6 Primordial nucleosynthesis

Time: 100 s to 1000 s

Temperature: 10^9 K to 3×10^8 K

Energy: 300 keV to 100 keV

As the temperature continued to decrease, protons and neutrons were able to combine to make light nuclei. This marked the beginning of the period referred to as the era of primordial **nucleosynthesis** (which literally means 'making nuclei'). The first such reaction to become energetically favoured was that of a single proton and neutron combining to produce a deuterium nucleus, with the excess energy carried away by a gamma-ray photon:

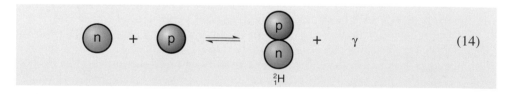

$$n + p \rightleftharpoons \begin{matrix} p \\ n \end{matrix} + \gamma \qquad (14)$$

$${}^2_1\text{H}$$

⬤ What is deuterium?

⬤ Recall from Chapter 2 that deuterium is an *isotope* of hydrogen. Whereas normal hydrogen nuclei consist simply of a proton, deuterium nuclei (sometimes called 'heavy hydrogen') contain a proton and a neutron.

At high temperatures (greater than 10^9 K), there are a lot of high-energy photons so this reaction is favoured to go from right to left. As a result, deuterium nuclei were rapidly broken down. However, as the temperature fell below 10^9 K when the Universe was about 100 s old, deuterium production was favoured. Virtually all of the remaining free neutrons in the Universe were rapidly bound up in deuterium nuclei, and from then on other light nuclei formed. One of the reactions that occurred was:

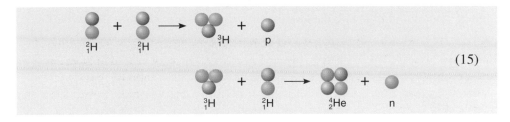

(15)

What is the nucleus represented by $^3_1$H?

This represents a nucleus of another isotope of hydrogen (called tritium), which contains two neutrons and one proton.

This shows that two deuterium nuclei react together to form a nucleus of tritium with the ejection of a proton. The tritium nucleus immediately reacts with another deuterium nucleus to form a nucleus of helium-4 with the emission of a neutron. The proton and neutron produced in the two reactions above can combine to form another deuterium nucleus, so the *net* result of this set of reactions is that two deuterium nuclei are converted into a single nucleus of helium-4.

Other more massive nuclei were also made as follows:

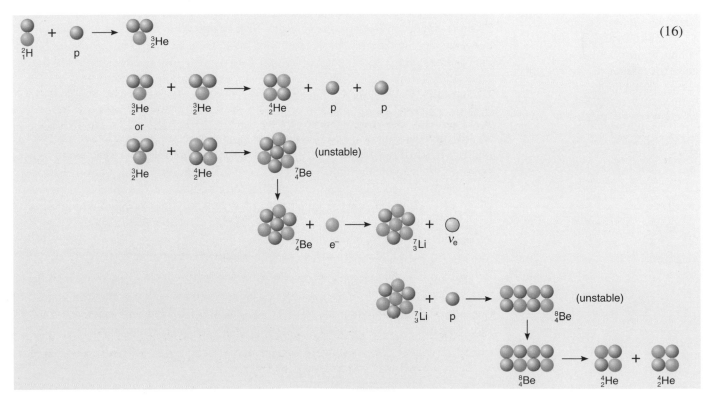

(16)

This shows that deuterium nuclei react with protons to make nuclei of helium-3. These can then either react with other helium-3 nuclei to make helium-4 plus more protons or with nuclei of helium-4 to make beryllium-7. Nuclei of beryllium-7 are unstable and immediately capture an electron to form lithium-7 with the emission of an electron neutrino. Lithium-7 nuclei can react further with a proton to create nuclei of beryllium-8, but these too are unstable and immediately split apart into a pair of helium-4 nuclei. The end products of the four reactions are nuclei of helium-3, helium-4 and lithium-7, with the vast majority ending up as helium-4.

⬤ The reactions in Equation 16 are the same as those that comprise the later stages of the proton–proton chain that occurs in the Sun (Chapter 9). Why did the first stage of the proton–proton chain not occur to any great extent in the early Universe?

◯ The first stage of the proton–proton chain relies on the weak interaction and takes, on average, 10^{10} years to occur for any individual pair of protons. In the early Universe at this epoch, there was just not enough time for this reaction to occur to any great extent over the period considered here.

Nuclei with a mass number greater than seven did not survive in the early Universe. This is because there are no stable nuclei with a mass number of eight — notice from above that the beryllium nuclei decay spontaneously, leading ultimately to more helium-4. The reactions that by-pass this bottleneck take much longer than the few minutes that were available for nucleosynthesis at this time. (Remember, we're now talking about a time-span of around 15 minutes when the Universe had an age of between 100 and 1000 s.) Before more advanced reactions could occur, the Universe cooled too much to provide the energy necessary to initiate them.

The ratio of protons to neutrons had, by this time, reached about seven protons for every one neutron. Because the neutrons were bound up in nuclei, they no longer decayed, and the ratio remained essentially fixed from here on. The vast majority of the neutrons ended up in nuclei of helium-4. Only very tiny fractions were left in deuterium, helium-3 and lithium-7 nuclei, since the reactions to produce them were far more likely to continue and produce helium-4 than they were to halt at these intermediate products.

By the time the Universe had cooled to a temperature of about 3×10^8 K after 1000 s, the particles had insufficient energy to undergo any more reactions. The era of primordial nucleosynthesis was at an end, and the proportion of the various light elements was fixed. The rates of reaction to form helium and the other light elements have been calculated, and the abundances predicted may be compared with the abundances of these nuclei that are observed in the Universe today. There is close agreement between theory and observation.

The close agreement between the theoretically predicted abundances of the light elements and the observed abundances in the Universe today is the third major piece of evidence, alongside the cosmic microwave background and the Hubble expansion, in favour of the hot big bang model for the origin of the Universe (see Section 4.3).

At an age of 1000 s, the Universe reached a state where its matter constituents were essentially as they are today. There are about 10^9 photons for every baryon (proton and neutron), and about seven protons and electrons for every one neutron. Neutrinos and antineutrinos continue to travel through the Universe unhindered by virtually anything they encounter.

Worked example 6

Assume that the Universe contains one neutron for every seven protons, and that all the neutrons are today bound up in nuclei of helium-4. (a) What are the relative numbers of hydrogen and helium nuclei in the Universe? (b) What are the relative percentages, by mass, of hydrogen and helium in the Universe?

Answer

(a) One way to calculate the answer is as follows. Imagine that you have a box containing 14 protons and two neutrons — the 7 : 1 ratio mentioned in the question. If a nucleus of helium-4 is made from two protons and two neutrons, there will be 12 protons remaining in the box, each of which can be considered as a hydrogen nucleus. Therefore there are 12 hydrogen nuclei for every one helium-4 nucleus in the Universe.

(b) Taking the mass of a helium-4 nucleus to be four units, and that of a hydrogen nucleus to be one unit, the relative masses of the helium-4 and hydrogen in the box are 4 and 12, respectively. The fraction of the mass in the box due to helium-4 is therefore 4/(4 + 12) = 0.25 or 25%, and that due to hydrogen is 12/(4 + 12) = 0.75 or 75%. (In fact the actual mass fraction of helium-4 that is predicted to have come out of the Big Bang is between about 22% and 24%.) ◀

11.7 Structure in the Universe

Time: 10^{10} s to 4.2×10^{17} s (300 years to 14 billion years)

Temperature: 10^5 K to 2.73 K

Energy: 30 eV to 7×10^{-4} eV

As the Universe cooled still further, nothing much happened for a few hundred years (between 1000 s and 10^{10} s). As the mean energy per particle fell below a few tens of electronvolts, so electrons began to combine with nuclei to form neutral atoms.

Gradually, as this electrically neutral matter accumulated, gravity began to take over as the dominant force operating in the Universe. Slight variations in the amount of matter and radiation in different regions meant that matter began to gather together into slightly denser clumps. These clumps provided the seeds from which galaxies later grew.

By the time the Universe had cooled to a temperature of 3000 K, about 300 000 years after the Big Bang, the mean energy of the photons had fallen to about 1 eV, and most of the matter in the Universe was in the form of neutral atoms. This was the trigger for another significant change in the behaviour of the Universe. The background radiation photons — those 10^9 photons for every particle left over from the annihilation epoch (matter and antimatter reactions) — interacted for the last time with matter in the Universe. When hydrogen atoms are in their ground state, photons with an energy of at least 10 eV are required in order to excite them to even the next energy level. So from this point on in the history of the Universe, photons were no longer absorbed by matter. After this time, the cosmic background radiation simply expanded freely with the Universe, cooling as it did so.

Figure 71 (a) This colour-coded map shows departures from uniformity in the cosmic microwave background radiation over the whole sky. The two panels correspond to two 'halves' of the sky, projected onto a flat picture. The scale represents the temperature either side of the mean temperature of 2.73 K. Violet regions are slightly cooler than the mean value of 2.73 K, red regions are slightly hotter, by about 100 microkelvin (μK). Most of the variations seen are believed to represent localized variations in the density of matter at a time 300 000 years after the Big Bang when this radiation interacted with matter for the last time. This map is the final result after four years operation of the COBE satellite. (b) This map, produced by the Wilkinson Microwave Anisotropy Probe (WMAP) satellite, was released in 2003. It shows the whole sky. Ripples in the temperature of the microwave background are seen here on much finer scales than was possible with COBE.

When the cosmic microwave background radiation is observed today, very slight irregularities are observed in its temperature and intensity. These reflect slight differences in the matter distribution of the Universe at the time of the last interaction between the background photons and atoms. At the time of the discovery of these irregularities by the COBE satellite (Chapter 4), they were described as 'wrinkles in the fabric of space–time' (Figure 71).

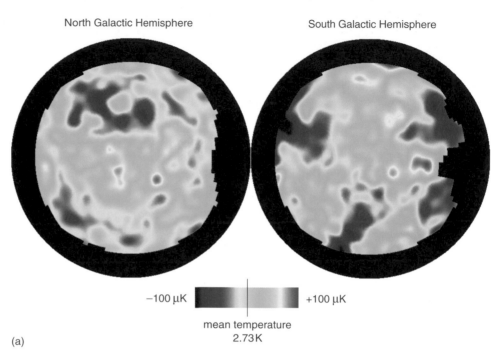

(a)

(b)

128

Some time after the last interaction of matter and radiation, but probably before the Universe was a billion years old, the first galaxies formed. The exact time for this event is uncertain, but within these early galaxies, stars condensed out of the gas to become dense enough for nuclear reactions to start within their cores. Deep within these stars, hydrogen was converted into helium, releasing energy as electromagnetic radiation into the Universe. As stars age, so their cores contract and grow hotter, allowing helium fusion to occur. These further reactions produce heavier nuclei, such as carbon, oxygen and silicon. Low-mass stars, like the Sun, will end their cosmic chemistry here. They will eventually simply run out of nuclear fuel, and their cores will collapse to form dense, compact objects called **white dwarfs**.

The more massive the star though, the hotter its interior, and the more massive the elements that can be produced by nuclear fusion reactions. But there is a limit to how far nuclear fusion can go. As you saw in Chapter 9, when four protons are converted into a nucleus of helium-4, the products have a lower mass than the reactants. This mass difference is liberated as energy. Similar mass reductions apply for reactions to produce all the elements up to those with mass numbers in the range of about 56 to 62, such as iron, cobalt and nickel. However, for nuclear fusion reactions beyond this, more energy must be put into the reactions than is released from them, so these are not viable.

As the most massive stars approach the ends of their lives, when their cores are composed of nuclei that undergo no more fusion, some nuclear reactions within their interiors release free neutrons. These neutrons can then add, slowly one at a time, to the iron, cobalt or nickel nuclei to make even more massive elements. As more and more neutrons are added, some transform into protons, via beta-minus decay, and in this way massive (stable) nuclei up to lead and bismuth can be created. These are the most massive, non-radioactive nuclei that exist in the Universe.

But what happens to these massive stars? When the core is largely composed of iron, they have no further source of energy available. The outer layers fall inwards, squeezing the centre of the star down until it has a density comparable to that of an atomic nucleus. The collapse halts — suddenly — and the material rebounds, setting off a shock wave back through the outer layers of the star. The result is a supernova explosion, in which 90% of the star's mass is thrown violently out into space (see Figure 72). The star's core left behind will be revealed as a **neutron star**, or the ultimate compact object, a **black hole**.

In the final moments of its life, the star has one final surprise left. The immense temperatures and pressures created during the explosion cause electrons and protons to react to form huge numbers of free neutrons. These neutrons enable elements to be built *beyond* the lead and bismuth limit. All naturally radioactive elements in the Universe (apart from those which are the decay products of even more massive radioactive nuclei) were formed in such supernovae explosions, and a large proportion of the others between nickel and bismuth were also created in these violent events.

From here the star cycle repeats — but this time with a slight difference. Stars that formed after the first generation had lived and died had a richer source of raw material. A star like the Sun was formed in a galaxy that had already seen at least one generation of massive stars born, live and die in supernovae explosions. The gas and dust from which the Sun formed, about 5 billion years ago, had therefore been enriched by heavier elements produced inside these earlier stars. This leads to the possibility of the formation of planets from the rubble left behind.

Figure 72 The Crab nebula, a supernova remnant in the constellation of Taurus. This expanding cloud of gas was thrown off in a supernova explosion when a massive star reached the end of its life. The cloud seen here is about three parsecs across. The exploding star was seen by Chinese astronomers on 4 July 1054, and was so bright that it remained visible in full daylight for 23 days.

The Earth itself formed from such debris. Every nucleus of carbon, oxygen, nitrogen and silicon found on the Earth and within living creatures was created inside the heart of an ancient star. Every nucleus of precious metal such as silver, gold and platinum was formed either from slow neutron capture in ageing stars, or by rapid neutron capture during the supernova explosions that mark their death. And so we come full circle back to the present day, about 14 billion years after the Big Bang, when the Universe has cooled to only 2.73 K.

Homing in on a fairly average spiral galaxy, we find a fairly average star somewhere out in one its spiral arms. Orbiting this star is a small rocky planet, two-thirds covered with water, and with an atmosphere rich in oxygen. On the surface of the planet are many living creatures, including members of one species who are so interested in the origin and complexity of the Universe that they build telescopes and particle accelerators with which to study it. They observe the expansion of the Universe by the redshift of distant galaxies, and the cooling of the Universe by the spectrum of its background radiation. Using particle accelerators they recreate extreme temperatures and examine particle reactions that have not occurred in the Universe for billions of years. The revelations of such experiments confirm that no epoch or location in the Universe is subject to any special dispensation. That at all times and all places the same physical principles hold, yet manifest themselves in a gloriously evolving diversity.

11.8 Summary and questions

The Universe was created at the instant of the Big Bang. As it has aged, the Universe has cooled and distances within it have increased. At the earliest times, the four fundamental interactions were unified, but as the temperature of the Universe decreased, so these interactions became distinct.

The earliest time about which anything can be said is the Planck time, when the gravitational interaction had a similar strength to the other fundamental interactions. Before this, the concept of 'time' itself may have no meaning.

Early in its history, the Universe is presumed to have undergone an extremely rapid period of expansion, known as inflation. One effect of this was to smooth out any irregularities, leading to today's remarkably uniform observable Universe.

The early Universe contained *almost* equal numbers of matter and antimatter particles (quarks and leptons). However, there was an asymmetry of a few parts per billion in favour of matter. The matter and antimatter underwent mutual annihilation and the result of this is that there are now about 10^9 photons for every matter particle in the Universe.

Equal numbers of protons and neutrons were initially produced in the Universe from the up and down quarks remaining after annihilation. However, free neutrons decay, and this reduced their number, leading to a Universe containing about seven protons for every neutron today.

All free neutrons were soon bound up within nuclei of deuterium, helium and lithium. The approximate distribution of mass in the Universe is about 25% helium-4 to 75% hydrogen, with small traces of other nuclei.

Neutrinos ceased to interact with the rest of the Universe soon after protons and neutrons were formed.

At 300 000 years after the Big Bang, when the temperature was about 3000 K, photons produced from the matter–antimatter annihilations had their last interaction with the matter of the Universe. These photons, redshifted by a factor of a thousand by the expansion of the Universe, form the cosmic microwave background that is observed today.

As the Universe cooled still further, galaxies and stars were able to form under the influence of gravity. Stars process light nuclei into heavier ones within their cores. The more massive stars then undergo supernova explosions, throwing material out into space ready to be included in later generations of stars and planets.

Remember, you can use the 'A history of the Universe' computer package to help you answer the following questions.

Question 28

Figure 69 shows how top and bottom quarks can decay into bottom and charm quarks, respectively. Following the patterns shown there, draw Feynman diagrams to represent: (a) the decay of a charm quark into a strange quark, and (b) the decay of a strange quark into an up quark. ◄

Question 29

Imagine a hypothetical Universe in which weak interactions do not exist and in which only first-generation quarks and leptons are present (i.e. there are no charm, strange, top or bottom quarks, and no muons, muon neutrinos, tauons or tauon neutrinos). Speculate about the ways in which such a Universe would be different from our own. Your answer should be no longer than about 100 words. ◄

Question 30

In addition to the 'barrier' at a mass number of eight, there are also no stable nuclei with a mass number of five. Using the building blocks available in the early Universe, what nuclei could you combine to try to create a nucleus with a mass number of five? ◄

Question 31

(a) Describe three times or sites at which nucleosynthesis has occurred in the history of the Universe.

(b) At which of these times or sites did most of the (i) helium, (ii) oxygen, and (iii) uranium in the Universe originate? ◄

Question 32

In which order did the following events occur in the history of the Universe? (*Hint*: Consider the energy required for each process.)

(i)   the formation of atoms

(ii)   the formation of light nuclei

(iii)   the formation of quarks and leptons

(iv)   the formation of protons and neutrons

(v)   the annihilation of electrons and positrons

(vi)   the annihilation of quarks and antiquarks

(vii)   neutrinos cease to interact further with matter or radiation

(viii) background photons cease to interact with matter ◄

Question 33

Summarize the contents of the Universe at the times corresponding to the end of each of Sections 11.2 to 11.7. ◄

Question 34

What are the three key pieces of observational evidence that support the idea of a hot big bang? Which of them do you think allows cosmologists to reach back furthest into the past, and why? ◄

The future of the Universe

Space...is big. Really big. You just won't believe how vastly hugely mind bogglingly big it is. I mean you may think it's a long way down the road to the chemist, but that's just peanuts to space.

Douglas Adams, 1955–2001, *The Hitch Hiker's Guide to the Galaxy*

So what is the future of the Universe? Will it go on expanding and cooling for ever? Or does it have another fate in store? The short answer is that no one knows for sure, but at least two possibilities can be suggested.

These questions may be considered with the help of an analogy, namely that of launching an object from the surface of a planet, as shown in Figure 73. If a rocket is launched with a small amount of kinetic energy, it will eventually fall back to Earth as gravity wins and pulls the rocket back. If the rocket is given a larger amount of kinetic energy, sufficient for it to exceed the speed required to escape from the Earth, the rocket will leave the Earth altogether and travel out into space.

As with the rocket, so with the Universe. The balancing act here is between the energy of the expansion of the Universe (the kinetic energy) and the gravitational energy of all the matter in the Universe. The situation is summarized in Figure 74. If the energy of the expansion is sufficient to overcome the gravitational pull, then the Universe will continue expanding forever — such a Universe is known as 'open'. If, on the other hand, the energy of expansion is not enough to overcome the gravitational pull, the expansion will gradually slow down, and ultimately reverse — such a Universe is known as 'closed'.

12.1 A closed Universe

A **closed Universe** is one in which gravity wins; it is *finite* in size at all times. The expansion that is currently observed would gradually slow down and eventually stop all together. This corresponds to the maximum separation shown for the closed Universe in Figure 74. But gravity doesn't give up there! The expansion would then *reverse* — all the matter in the Universe would begin to converge as the Universe contracts. The contraction would gradually speed up and all the galaxies and clusters would rush towards each other.

⬤ What form would the Hubble law take after the contraction phase had been underway for some time?

◯ All distant galaxies would eventually exhibit a *blueshift* with the *approach* speed proportional to the distance away.

During the contraction, all the processes of the Big Bang outlined Chapter 11 would follow in reverse order! The atoms would ionize under the impact of radiation; then the nuclei would be smashed apart into protons and neutrons; finally the nucleons themselves would disintegrate into their constituent quarks. Photons would spontaneously create pairs of particles and antiparticles until equal amounts of radiation and matter again filled the Universe. As the temperature of the contracting Universe rose, so the four interactions would each in turn become indistinguishable as the unifications proceeded in reverse order.

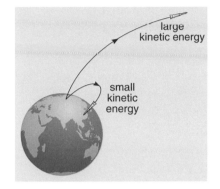

Figure 73 Possibilities for the path of a rocket launched from the Earth's surface.

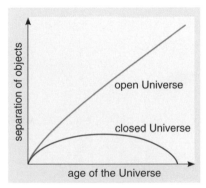

Figure 74 The way in which separations between objects vary with time in open and closed Universes. An open Universe expands forever, and so separations between clusters of galaxies continually increase. A closed Universe eventually begins to contract, whereupon the separations between clusters of galaxies would reduce.

133

Ultimately things would reach a mirror image of the Big Bang — known as a 'Big Crunch'. And what would happen next? Well, one possibility is that's the end of everything — no more matter, no more space, no more time. The Universe just ends.

But maybe not … Some cosmologists suggest that what happens instead is a kind of 'Big Bounce'. At the very last instant, the whole sequence would turn around and a new Big Bang would happen. There would be a whole new period of expansion and contraction, repeating the history of the Universe again and again, over and over, for ever more. What we know as *the* Big Bang may simply be the latest in an infinite series of Big Bounces that is set to repeat an infinite number of times. We revisit the very latest ideas on this topic at the end of the book.

12.2 An open Universe

An **open Universe** is one in which gravity loses, so that the separation between objects would continue to increase for ever; it would be *infinite* in size at all times. It would have been infinite in size at the instant of the Big Bang, and would remain infinite in size as space expands and the separation between galaxies increases. However, in the future of such an ever-expanding Universe, all the stars would eventually run out of nuclear fuel.

- What is the end-point in the life of a star when it has run out of nuclear fuel?

- Low-mass stars (such as the Sun) will evolve into compact objects called white dwarfs. More massive stars will undergo supernova explosions, before ending up as either neutron stars or black holes.

These dead stars, along with any planets and other pieces of rock and dust, would gradually spiral in towards the centres of their respective galaxies where they would be consumed by the massive black holes that most astronomers believe exist in all galaxies. So, at this point the Universe would be cold and dead, containing nothing but black holes and cosmic background photons, but still continuing to expand.

You may think that this is the end of the story — but not so. The name black hole was given to these objects in the belief that nothing — not even light — can escape from them, so they would literally appear to be a black hole in space. But the cosmologist Stephen Hawking has shown that black holes are not entirely black. By a neat trick of quantum physics, black holes will eventually 'evaporate' into a swarm of subatomic particles and antiparticles. The process, however, takes an extremely long time — a black hole with the mass of a whole galaxy will take about 10^{97} years to evaporate! But that's okay, because the Universe has an infinite time to expand in this scenario. These particles and antiparticles would eventually mutually annihilate each other, each pair creating photons of electromagnetic radiation. So, the *final* fate of an open Universe is that it contains just photons, and simply becomes more and more dilute as the expansion continues. This is known as the heat death of the Universe.

12.3 A compromise

- Referring to the earlier discussion of launching a rocket from the surface of the Earth, what would happen to the rocket if it were launched with insufficient kinetic energy to cause it to leave the Earth for good, but just enough to prevent it from falling back again?

⬤ The rocket would go into a stable orbit around the Earth.

By analogy with this, there is also a third possibility for the fate of the Universe — called by cosmologist John Barrow the 'British Compromise Universe'. This is a Universe that is not quite open, but not quite closed either. After all, if there are these two extremes — the closed Universe in which gravity wins and the open Universe in which expansion wins — there must be a critical situation in between the two in which the energy of expansion is *exactly* balanced by the gravitational pull. One proton more and gravity would win, leading to a big crunch; one proton less in this Universe and the expansion would win, leading to the heat death scenario. In this model, more properly called a **flat Universe** model, the entire Universe is infinite in size at all times, just as in the open Universe model. However, it has the interesting consequence that although the rate of expansion continues to slow down, it only reaches zero expansion rate at an infinite time in the future, at which point all objects in the Universe have an infinite separation.

In the picture just outlined, just which type of Universe we are in depends crucially on the mean density of matter in the Universe. The **critical density** is defined as that which corresponds to the flat Universe. If the Hubble constant is currently $72 \, km \, s^{-1} \, Mpc^{-1}$, then the critical density is currently equivalent to about four protons per cubic metre. If the actual mean density is less than the critical value, the Universe is open; if the actual mean density is greater than the critical value, the Universe is closed.

A crucial result of Alan Guth's inflation theory, discussed in Section 11.3, is that the very rapid expansion drives the Universe to be flat. Any deviations from the critical density that may have existed before inflation, are smoothed out by the inflationary process, resulting in a Universe with almost *exactly* the critical density, to an accuracy of better than one part in a million. In other words, if the inflation theory is correct, we live in an infinite flat Universe.

12.4 Acceleration and deceleration

From the preceding discussion you might conclude that the consensus amongst astronomers is that the expansion of the Universe has continuously slowed down, or decelerated, since the time of inflation, and the Universe is now following the expansion rate described by the 'flat' Universe model. The Universe will expand forever but at an ever-decreasing rate, such that objects reach an infinite separation at an infinite time in the future.

Well, that *was* the accepted picture of the Universe until 1998. In that year, evidence began to appear that the expansion rate of the Universe may not be as straightforward as astronomers had previously believed. The new observational evidence was based around measurements made of supernovae in distant galaxies.

As you know, supernovae are the result of exploding stars. One sort, known as **type II supernovae**, are believed to be caused by massive stars reaching the ends of their lives, and exploding when they cannot undergo any more energy-releasing fusion reactions in their cores. But another sort, **type Ia supernovae**, are something quite different. Their spectra show no evidence of hydrogen and they all seem to reach the *same* luminosity. And this is where their usefulness as a standard candle and a probe of the distant Universe comes in. If they all have the same luminosity, and astronomers know what that luminosity is, and if their apparent brightness (or flux)

Figure 75　The brightness of distant supernovae plotted against their redshift. (Note that brightness increases *downwards* in this graph.) The brightness that would be expected if the Universe was expanding according to a conventional flat Universe model is shown by the solid line. The more distant supernovae are significantly *fainter* than this prediction.

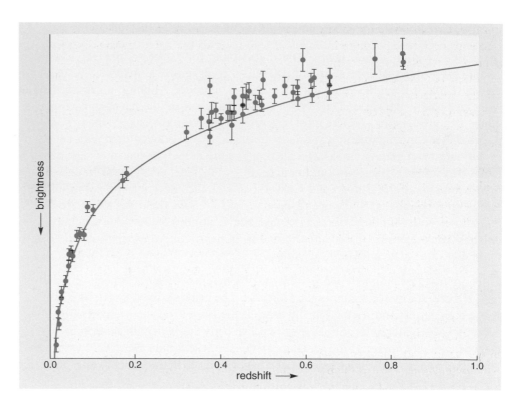

can be measured, then astronomers can calculate how far away they are. Furthermore, by looking at the relative positions of lines in their spectra, astronomers can also measure their redshift. So in principle, astronomers can measure both how far away type Ia supernovae and their host galaxies are *and* how fast their host galaxies are receding from us.

In 1998, astronomers from the Supernova Cosmology Project, led by Saul Perlmutter of the Lawrence Berkeley Laboratory in California, reported measurements of 42 distant type Ia supernovae. These supernovae had redshifts between about 0.3 and 0.8, so light from them was emitted between about 3 and 5 billion years ago. Figure 75 shows the results of plotting the maximum brightness of these supernovae against their redshift. It shows that these distant supernovae are about 15–25% *fainter* than they ought to be if the Universe had simply followed the expansion rate predicted by the conventional flat Universe model. The proposed explanation for why these supernovae appear fainter than expected is that the light from the supernova explosions has travelled a greater distance than is predicted by the conventional model. The researchers suggest that the reason for this is that the Universe's expansion *speeded up* whilst the light from the supernovae was on its way to the Earth, so the amount of expansion has been greater than predicted by the conventional model.

> In other words, the expansion of the Universe is currently speeding up (accelerating), not slowing down (decelerating), as everyone had assumed until now.

If this is true, astronomers realized that it suggests the presence of a mysterious form of 'negative gravity' or so called **dark energy,** which *opposes* the gravitational attraction of matter that was assumed to be responsible for the deceleration of the

Universal expansion. Dark energy seems to be a property of empty space — even space with no matter particles in it — and is sometimes known as **quintessence**. This is a word meaning literally 'fifth essence' and follows the ancient idea of the 'four elements' of earth, air, fire and water. Dark energy behaves rather differently from the matter in the Universe. As space expands, the density of matter must get progressively less and less as things become farther and farther apart. However, the dark energy of empty space can remain *undiluted* by this expansion and so exert a significant effect on the expansion rate of the Universe.

In fact, 'negative gravity' is not a new idea. Albert Einstein himself first suggested the idea when he developed his general theory of relativity in 1915. Having derived the equations that describe the overall behaviour of the Universe, Einstein was concerned that his equations did not allow a static Universe to exist. According to the equations of general relativity, the Universe had to be either expanding or contracting. At that time there was no evidence that the Universe was anything but static, so Einstein introduced an extra term into his equations which he called Λ (the Greek upper case lambda) — the so-called **cosmological constant**. This took the form of a sort of negative gravity and was assumed to be just strong enough to counteract the pull of gravity and so result in a static Universe. When, a few years later, Edwin Hubble announced his evidence that the Universe is in fact expanding and not static at all, Einstein is said to have commented that the introduction of the cosmological constant was the biggest blunder of his life. However, in the light of the type Ia supernova results, maybe Einstein was on the right track after all…

Before we get carried away with this idea though, it is worth looking at these supernova results more closely. First, the values for the brightnesses of the distant supernovae are rather uncertain, and it is still just about conceivable that the conventional expansion rate would fit the data. Secondly, there is the calibration problem. Astronomers need to know the maximum apparent brightness of the supernova, but comparing supernovae at different redshifts means that different parts of the supernova spectrum are shifted into or out of the spectral range that is used to measure the brightness (say the optical range between about 400 nm and 700 nm). This effect must be corrected for in order to work out the actual maximum brightness in a comparable way for all type Ia supernovae whatever their redshift, and clearly there is the potential for uncertainties in the calibration process. Thirdly, astronomers must also take account of the amount of absorption that the light from the supernovae has experienced as it travels huge distances across the Universe. More absorption, caused say by extra dust in the vicinity of the supernova itself, could also make the distant supernovae appear fainter than expected. Even if these problems are solved though, there is still one more difficulty. Just what *are* these type Ia supernovae and how can we be sure they all *do* have the same luminosity?

12.5 Type Ia supernovae

The short answer is that no-one really knows exactly what type Ia supernovae actually are. What is fairly clear is that they are the result of white dwarfs that somehow get pushed over the maximum mass at which they can survive. As noted earlier in Section 11.7, white dwarfs are the dead cores of low-mass stars. They are supported against collapse due to gravity by a quantum physics phenomenon called **electron degeneracy pressure**. It turns out that this effect is unable to support a white dwarf against collapse if the white dwarf mass is greater than about 1.4 times the mass of the Sun. Astronomers write this as $1.4M_\odot$, which may be read as

'1.4 solar masses', and this is known as the **Chandrasekhar limit**. So the idea is that some white dwarfs suddenly find themselves with greater than $1.4M_\odot$ and so collapse, giving rise to a supernova explosion. Since all white dwarfs have the same maximum mass, this is supposed to be the reason why all type Ia supernovae have the same luminosity. But what are these objects *before* they go bang?

One idea is that they are a binary star system consisting of a pair of white dwarfs whose combined mass is greater than $1.4M_\odot$. As the stars orbit each other, they lose energy by radiating gravitational waves and gradually spiral together. When they get close enough, the two white dwarfs merge and a type Ia supernova is the result.

Alternatively, type Ia supernovae may arise in another type of binary star — one in which a white dwarf constantly pulls material from a companion star (Figure 76). The strong gravitational field of the white dwarf is able to tear its companion apart, and gradually more and more mass is deposited on the white dwarf surface. Some of this material undergoes nuclear fusion on the white dwarf surface and may be blown away from the system. However, more accumulates than is lost, so the mass of the white dwarf steadily increases. The white dwarf eventually reaches a mass greater than $1.4M_\odot$ and a type Ia supernovae is the result.

Figure 76   An interacting binary star in which a white dwarf pulls material from its companion. The white dwarf sits at the centre of the flattened structure known as an accretion disc. The companion star is distorted into a pear-shape by the gravitational pull of the white dwarf.

Astronomers do see examples both of binary white dwarfs and of white dwarfs pulling material off companion stars and undergoing constant nuclear fusion on their surfaces in our local neighbourhood of the Galaxy. Either, or possibly both, of these types of system may be the source of type Ia supernovae in our Galaxy and in other galaxies throughout the Universe. But will both give rise to type Ia supernovae of the *same* luminosity? And will that luminosity always be the same at all times in the Universe's history (and so at all redshifts)?

The chemical composition of the Universe has certainly changed with time as later generations of stars have formed from material that has been enriched by heavy elements formed in, and expelled by, earlier supernovae. Might the changing chemical composition mean that modern (nearby) type Ia supernovae are intrinsically *less luminous* than ancient (distant) type Ia supernovae? At the time of writing, no-one knows the answers to any of these questions, although there is a great deal of current research being devoted to finding out the answers.

12.6 The smoking gun

An indication that the acceleration and dark energy idea may be correct came in April 2001. Adam Riess of the Space Telescope Science Institute was studying images of the Hubble Deep Field. These were the deepest exposure images ever made by the Hubble Space Telescope and so contained some of the faintest and most distant galaxies ever seen. By comparing two images, taken in 1995 and 1997, Riess discovered the most distant supernova ever seen (Figure 77). It was a type Ia supernova and it had a redshift of 1.7, which means that the light from it was emitted when the Universe was only a few billion years old.

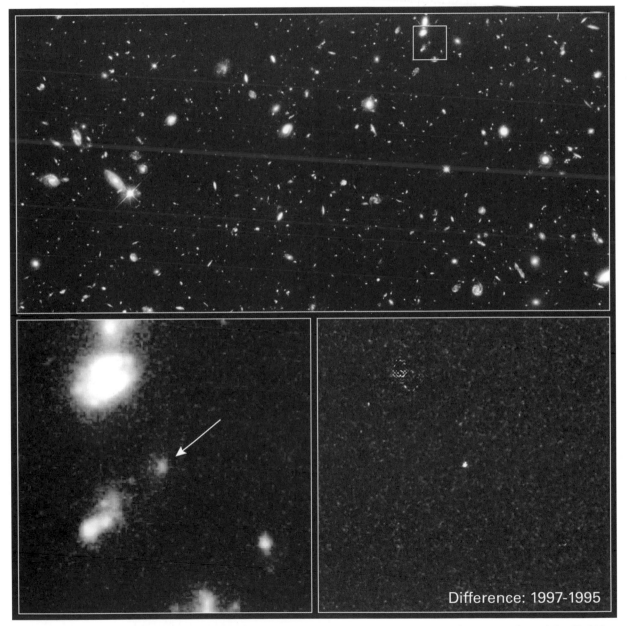

Figure 77   The most distant supernova ever seen. The top picture, taken in 1997, shows a region of the Hubble Deep Field image, while the lower left picture is a close-up of the region containing the supernova. The picture in the bottom right shows the result of subtracting an image taken in 1995 from the one taken in 1997 to reveal the supernova that exploded between one picture being taken and the next.

The extraordinary thing is that the maximum brightness of this supernova is roughly twice as large as it should be! So this supernova must be significantly *closer* than it would be if the Universe had expanded at a steady rate.

The proposed explanation for this is as follows. Soon after the Big Bang, when the Universe was only a few billion years old, galaxies were relatively close together and their gravitational pull was sufficient to slow down the expansion of the Universe and so produce a deceleration. A supernova that exploded during this period, such as the one whose discovery was announced in April 2001, would thus be closer to us now than suggested by its measured redshift. As the Universe aged and galaxies grew farther apart, dark energy was able to win out over the gravitational attraction, so making the Universe expand ever faster and turning the deceleration into an acceleration.

As astronomers look further back in time they should see the (current) acceleration turn into a deceleration – and this is just what the various observations of type Ia supernovae seem to be implying! The supernovae observed by Saul Perlmutter in the redshift range 0.3–0.8 are fainter than expected (they are in the nearby, recent, accelerating Universe), whilst that measured by Adam Riess at a redshift of 1.7 is brighter than expected (it is in the more distant, early, decelerating Universe).

Confirmation of the above theory must await the discovery of more distant supernovae, and until then it would be unwise to revise the whole history of the Universe based on just these few observations. However, let us for the moment explore the consequences for the Universe if these type Ia supernovae measurements and their interpretation are correct.

12.7 Matter and energy in the Universe

As mentioned earlier, inflation implies that the Universe is 'flat' and as such its density should be equal to the critical density. Astronomers indicate this by saying that the actual density divided by the critical density is equal to one, or in symbols $\Omega = 1$ where Ω is the Greek capital letter **omega** — the last letter of the alphabet.

If this critical density is all accounted for by matter, then astronomers say that 'omega matter' is equal to one, i.e. $\Omega_M = 1$. However, the recent type Ia supernovae results imply that there is another sort of density acting in the Universe – the density of dark energy, represented by 'omega lambda' Ω_Λ. Dark energy can also contribute to the density of the Universe since, according to Einstein's famous equation $E = mc^2$, mass and energy are interchangeable. It is possible to have a flat but open Universe that expands forever at an increasing rate, if

$$\Omega_M + \Omega_\Lambda = 1 \tag{17}$$

So what do the latest results imply for omega matter and omega lambda? The best agreement with the type Ia supernovae data and with results from observations of the cosmic microwave background announced in 2003 (Figure 71b) is found to be a Universe with Ω_M equal to about 0.27 and Ω_Λ equal to about 0.73. But what evidence is there that the Universe contains an amount of matter equal to 27% of the critical density, implied by $\Omega_M \sim 0.27$?

140

Adding up the amount of matter implied by all the stars and galaxies in the observable Universe, astronomers conclude that the fraction of the critical density accounted for by **luminous matter** is only about 0.5%. Even massive black holes, presumed to exist in the centres of galaxies, can only account for another 0.0001% or so of the critical density, so their contribution is negligible.

However, that's not the end of the story. Astronomers also believe that there is **dark matter** in the Universe, some of which makes its presence felt by the motion of stars in the outer regions of some galaxies. Dark matter, as its name suggests, cannot be seen. Some fraction of it may be in the form of low-mass dead stars, that were never able to undergo nuclear fusion, and which are situated in the halos of all galaxies. Searches for these 'massive compact halo objects' (known as **MaCHOs** for short), in the outer regions of our Galaxy are currently underway, and beginning to bear fruit. This type of dark matter is referred to as **baryonic dark matter** because it is made up of the familiar protons and neutrons, just like luminous matter. It is believed, though, that even the dark-matter MaCHOs can account for only 4% of the critical density. So where is the other missing 23% or so of the critical matter density?

This is the famous **missing mass** problem. Quite simply the implication is that a huge fraction of the matter in the Universe is made of some, so far unknown, constituents that may be totally unlike the rest of the protons, neutrons and electrons from which the familiar contents of the Universe are built. This is called **non-baryonic dark matter**, often referred to as 'weakly interacting massive particles' (or **WIMPs** for short) and a great deal of effort is currently being expended on searching for it!

12.8 Born out of fire: an alternative to the Big Bang?

Before we finish our exploration of how the Universe works, we must mention a current challenger to the title of the theory for the origin of the Universe. The material presented in this section is absolutely at the forefront of current scientific understanding. It is also even more bizarre than anything we have presented so far! So sit back and prepare for a final roller coaster ride to the frontiers of modern physics.

The **ekpyrotic Universe** is the name given to a remarkable new theory that provides an interesting alternative to the standard inflationary, hot big bang model that has permeated the last two chapters of this book. 'Ekpyrotic' is a Greek word that comes from an ancient idea that the Universe is continually destroyed and then recreated by fire in an endless cycle. The new theory provides an explanation for the origin of the hot big bang and does away with the need for a period of inflation (Section 11.3). It is also intricately linked with the ideas in M-theory about superunification discussed in Section 10.3 and provides perhaps the ultimate link between particle physics and cosmology. In this spirit it serves as an ideal topic on which to finish our story.

The ekpyrotic Universe theory was proposed in 2001 by Justin Khoury, Burt Ovrut, Paul Steinhardt and Neil Turok. In their model, the hot big bang was more like a **Big Clap** in which two four-dimensional branes collided together. The effect of the collision was to produce the energy, matter and structure that we now see in the Universe around us.

As noted in Section 10.3, M-theory predicts that branes exist in 11 dimensions. Six of these dimensions are curled up too small for us to see, but allow strings to vibrate and so give rise to the various fundamental particles. In practice, we can therefore forget about these six tiny dimensions when thinking on cosmological scales. Our visible Universe, with its three dimensions of space and one of time, accounts for a total of four dimensions. The suggestion of the ekpyrotic Universe model is that there is also a fifth dimension (a fourth spatial dimension) all around us that is actually relatively large, and we don't see it because only gravity can exist there. In fact, the reason gravity is so weak when compared with the other three fundamental interactions may be because some of its effect 'leaks out' into this fifth dimension.

○ To recap, account for all 11 dimensions in M-theory, according to the ekpyrotic Universe scenario.

○ Six dimensions are curled up too small to see; three dimensions are the regular spatial dimensions we experience; one dimension is that of time; and the remaining dimension, making 11 in all, is an extra spatial dimension that we can't experience because only gravity can exist there.

In the ekpyrotic Universe model, our Universe sits on a **visible brane** but there is also a nearby **hidden brane**. The hidden brane is parallel to our Universe, but separated at a constant distance from it across the fifth dimension. Particles within the hidden brane interact with particles in our visible brane only through gravity, via the fifth dimension. They may therefore behave like WIMPs. Hiding the non-baryonic dark matter on the hidden brane is an attractive idea, and might explain why it is such difficult stuff to locate!

Initially, the visible brane is cold and empty. Then, at some time, the hidden brane shrugs off a lighter brane (like a snake shedding its skin) called a **bulk brane**. This bulk brane travels across the fifth dimension and collides violently with the visible brane (Figure 78) before bouncing off. These branes have mass and so possess kinetic energy. When the branes collide, their enormous kinetic energy is liberated as heat and appears as the hot fireball we have hitherto thought of as the Big Bang.

Figure 78   The hidden brane shrugs off a bulk brane, which collides violently with the visible brane. Because of ripples in the bulk brane, the collision happens at slightly different times in different places.

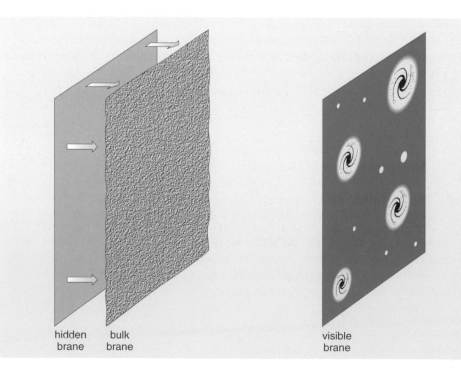

hidden brane   bulk brane   visible brane

The enormous temperature creates matter and antimatter particles via pair creation mechanisms, just as described earlier. The collision also triggers the expansion of space within the visible brane.

The colliding branes are initially flat in the sense that we described in Section 12.3, but there are *ripples* in the bulk brane, caused by random fluctuations at the quantum level. So when the collision happens, it occurs at slightly different times in different places. These ripples in the bulk brane therefore produce variations in the density of the Universe at different places and so ultimately give rise to the departures from uniformity in the cosmic microwave background radiation that we see today (Figure 71), and from there grow to become superclusters of galaxies. From here on, the Universe will evolve just as we have already described in Sections 11.4 to 11.7, but the need for inflation has disappeared. The way the four fundamental interactions become separate as the Universe cools, the nucleosynthesis of the light elements and the production of the cosmic microwave background, all follow the pattern we have already outlined.

However, there is one last surprise in store from the ekpyrotic Universe. Between the visible brane and the hidden brane, there is a vacuum, and the vacuum acts like a spring between the branes. Within our Universe, sitting on the visible brane, the effect of the vacuum is to create a repulsive gravitational force that we describe by the cosmological constant (Section 12.4) and attribute to dark energy. Between the branes though, the vacuum force acts as an attraction between them. Today the spring is still being stretched, but eventually it will reach its maximum extension and the branes will start to speed towards each other. Then there will be another collision, another Big Clap. Notice though that this is not quite the same as the Big Bang/Big Crunch scenario that we discussed in Section 12.1. In the ekpyrotic Universe, the oscillation only happens in the hidden fifth dimension, between the branes. From the point of view of someone stuck on the visible brane (like us) space just keeps expanding, though the expansion keeps getting another push from each successive Big Clap. It is only from the point of view of the hidden fifth dimension that the Universe appears to be cyclic.

Each 'cycle' of the Universe, as it appears to us on the visible brane, is like that of an open or flat Universe. Space continues to expand; stars and galaxies evolve to the ends of their lives and eventually end up consumed by supermassive black holes. The black holes may eventually evaporate into subatomic particles, which then mutually annihilate each other, leading to a dilute sea of photons filling all of space. It is only then, when the Universe has become cold and virtually empty, that the vacuum spring between the branes gives rise to another Big Clap, and the whole process starts again. Matter and radiation are produced from the heat energy liberated from the kinetic energy of the branes, and the whole cosmic evolution of the Universe can happen again. And again. And again. And again. It is a suitably inspiring or humbling thought, depending on how you view it, to realize that 'our Universe' may simply be the current version of an infinite cycle of Universes stretching for ever into the past and into the infinite future.

12.9 Summary and questions

There are three possibilities for the fate of the Universe. Just which type of Universe we are in depends crucially on the density of matter within it. If the density is greater than the critical density, the Universe is closed; if the density is less than the critical density, the Universe is open; if the density is equal to the critical density, the Universe is flat.

A closed Universe is finite in size. Gravity will eventually halt the expansion of such a Universe and then reverse it. The ultimate fate of a closed Universe is a Big Crunch in which it collapses, or a Big Bounce in which the whole cycle of expansion, contraction and crunch repeats.

An open Universe is infinite in size at all times. The expansion of such a Universe will continue into the infinite future. The entire matter content of an open Universe will eventually be consumed by massive black holes that ultimately evaporate in a stream of matter and antimatter particles. The final fate of an open Universe is an infinitely dilute sea of photons.

It is most probable that we live in a 'compromise' flat Universe in which the kinetic energy of expansion is exactly balanced by the gravitational energy of the matter within it.

Observations of distant type Ia supernovae seem to imply that the expansion of the Universe is currently accelerating, although it may have had a phase of deceleration in the distant past. These observations imply that the Universe contains dark energy, which can counteract the pull of gravity on large scales.

The best estimates for the contributions of the various constituents of the Universe to the overall critical density are that $\Omega_M + \Omega_\Lambda = 1$ where matter contributes $\Omega_M = 0.27$ and dark energy contributes $\Omega_\Lambda = 0.73$. The matter component is probably made up as follows: about 0.005 from luminous matter (stars, galaxies, etc.), about 0.04 from baryonic dark matter (MaCHOs), and about 0.23 from non-baryonic dark matter (WIMPs).

The very latest idea for the origin of the Universe is the ekpyrotic Universe model. In this scenario, the Big Bang was caused by the collision of two four-dimensional branes. Successive collisions of these branes give rise to a succession of Big Claps, and between each of these the Universe expands just as in a conventional open or flat Universe model, but without the need for a period of inflation. Our Universe sits on the visible brane and is parallel to the hidden brane, but separated from it across the fifth dimension by a region containing a vacuum. The energy of this vacuum is responsible for the current accelerated expansion of the Universe.

Question 35

Write a few sentences to summarize the main differences between the properties of a closed Universe and an open Universe. ◄

Question 36

Write a few sentences summarizing the evidence that our Universe is currently experiencing a phase of accelerated expansion. ◄

Question 37

Why are type Ia supernovae believed to be 'standard candles'? ◄

Question 38

Write a few sentences summarizing what is meant by each of the following terms:
(a) luminous matter, (b) baryonic dark matter, (c) non-baryonic dark matter,
(d) dark energy in relation to the contents of the Universe, assuming a conventional
Big Bang model. ◄

Question 39

In the cyclic ekpyrotic Universe model, how are non-baryonic dark matter and dark
energy explained? ◄

Question 40

In the cyclic ekpyrotic Universe model, how old and how big is the Universe? ◄

What we have learned is like a handful of earth. What we have yet to learn is
like the whole world.

Avvaiyar, 9th century

Questions: answers and comments

Chapter 1

Question 1

(a) In order of increasing size, the numbers are: 10^{-4}, 3×10^{-4}, 10^{-3}, 3×10^{-3}, 10^4, 3×10^4.

(b) 10^{25} is 100 times (or 10^2 times) bigger than 10^{23}.

(c) Since 1 m = 1000 mm (or 10^3 mm), 300 m is equivalent to 300×10^3 mm or 3×10^5 mm. Since 1 km = 1000 m or 1 m = 10^{-3} km, 300 m is equivalent to 300×10^{-3} km = 3×10^{-1} km or 0.3 km.

Question 2

$$10^8 \times 10^5 = 10^{(8+5)} = 10^{13}$$

$$10^9 \times 10^{-4} = 10^{(9-4)} = 10^5$$

$$10^{-11} \times 10^{-6} = 10^{(-11-6)} = 10^{-17}$$

$$10^9/10^3 = 10^{(9-3)} = 10^6$$

$$10^7/10^{12} = 10^{(7-12)} = 10^{-5}$$

$$10^{-4}/10^{-13} = 10^{-4-(-13)} = 10^9$$

Chapter 2

Question 3

(a) Since the atomic number of iron is 26, the nucleus contains 26 protons. Since the mass number is 56, the total number of protons and neutrons in the nucleus is 56, and so the nucleus contains 56 − 26 = 30 neutrons. (b) An electrically neutral atom contains the same number of electrons as protons, so the atom contains 26 electrons. (c) Each proton and neutron has a mass energy of about 1 GeV, whereas each electron has a mass energy of only 500 keV or 0.0005 GeV. The electrons' mass energy is therefore negligible and the mass energy of the iron-56 atom is roughly 56×1 GeV = 56 GeV.

Question 4

(a) You have seen that the quark content of a proton is (uud), so the antiquark content of an antiproton must be ($\overline{\text{uu}}\overline{\text{d}}$) Now, the charge of an antiquark is opposite to that of the corresponding quark. So the charge of a $\overline{\text{u}}$ antiquark is −2/3 unit and the charge of a $\overline{\text{d}}$ antiquark is +1/3 unit. The charge of an antiproton is therefore − 2/3 − 2/3 + 1/3 = −1 unit. This is the opposite charge to that of a proton, as expected.

(b) Similarly, you have seen that the quark content of a neutron is (udd), so the antiquark content of an antineutron must be ($\overline{\text{u}}\overline{\text{dd}}$). Using the values for the charge of a $\overline{\text{u}}$ antiquark and a $\overline{\text{d}}$ antiquark from above, the charge of an antineutron is therefore − 2/3 + 1/3 + 1/3 = 0. Notice that this is the *same* as the charge of a neutron, even though the antineutron is composed of antiquarks.

Question 5

A baryon consists of three quarks and quarks have an electric charge of either +2/3 or −1/3 unit. So the electric charge of a baryon can be any of:

$$+2/3 + 2/3 + 2/3 = +6/3 = +2 \text{ units}$$

$$+2/3 + 2/3 - 1/3 = +3/3 = +1 \text{ unit}$$

$$+2/3 - 1/3 - 1/3 = 0$$

$$-1/3 - 1/3 - 1/3 = -1 \text{ unit}$$

Notice that these are all *whole* numbers.

Chapter 3

Question 6

(a) A wave model of light is used to explain its propogation through space whereas a particle model is used to explain its interaction with atoms.

(b) In order of increasing photon energy, the sequence is: radio waves, microwaves, infrared radiation, red light, yellow light, blue light, ultraviolet radiation, X-rays, gamma-rays. In order of increasing wavelength, the sequence is exactly reversed.

(c) (i) The mass-energies of an electron and positron are each about 500 keV, so the two photons produced by the annihilation will each have an energy of about 500 keV. (ii) Photons of this energy lie near to the boundary between X-rays and gamma-rays in the electromagnetic spectrum.

Question 7

The light from a sodium street lamp is an emission line spectrum. Conversely, the spectral distribution of the light from a tungsten filament light bulb is a continuous spectrum. So, the spectral distribution of the light from a tungsten filament light bulb after passing through a sodium vapour will be a continuous spectrum with two absorption lines superimposed, whose wavelengths correspond exactly to the wavelengths of the emission lines in the sodium lamp spectrum. This spectral distribution is shown in Figure 79.

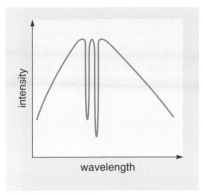

Figure 79 The spectral distribution of the light from a tungsten filament light bulb after passing through a sodium vapour.

Question 8

(a) Since 1 pc ~ 3×10^{13} km, a distance of 200 Mpc is equivalent to about $200 \times 10^6 \times 3 \times 10^{13}$ km = 6×10^{21} km.

(b) Since 1 pc ~ 3 ly, a distance of 200 Mpc is equivalent to $200 \times 10^6 \times 3 = 6 \times 10^8$ light years. So a beam of light would take 600 million years to travel from the cluster of galaxies to Earth.

Question 9

(a) According to Equation 4b, the redshift is equal to: speed of galaxy/speed of light. So in this case we have: redshift = 0.6 km s^{-1}/3×10^5 km s^{-1} = 2×10^{-6}. (Redshift is a pure number and so has no unit.)

(b) The shift in wavelength is the difference between the observed wavelength and the rest wavelength. This may be determined using Equation 3b, change in wavelength = redshift × original wavelength. So in this case, change in wavelength = $(2 \times 10^{-6} \times 656$ nm$) = 1.3 \times 10^{-3}$ nm. This is a tiny shift, and for this reason the Doppler effect with light is not normally noticeable in everyday situations.

Question 10

(a) Since the wavelength of the light from the galaxy is shifted towards longer wavelengths, i.e. towards the red, the galaxy must be receding from the Earth.

(b) According to Equation 3a, redshift = change in wavelength/original wavelength. In this case, redshift = $(500.7 - 486.1)$ nm/486.1 nm = 0.03.

(c) Equation 4a states that speed of galaxy = redshift × speed of light, so here speed of galaxy = $0.03 \times 3 \times 10^5$ km s^{-1} = 9×10^3 km s^{-1}.

Question 11

(a) The first step is to calculate the recession speed of the galaxy by using Equation 5a: speed of galaxy = Hubble constant × distance to galaxy. Taking the Hubble constant as 72 km s^{-1} Mpc^{-1} and the distance as 40 Mpc, the speed of the galaxy is (72 km s^{-1} Mpc^{-1}) × (400 Mpc) = 2.88×10^4 km s^{-1}. The redshift of this galaxy can be found from Equation 4b: redshift = speed of galaxy/speed of light, so redshift = 2.88×10^4 km s^{-1}/3×10^5 km s^{-1} = 0.096.

(b) The first step is to calculate the recession speed of the galaxy using Equation 4a: speed of galaxy = redshift × speed of light, so in this case speed of galaxy = $0.12 \times 3 \times 10^5$ km s^{-1} = 3.6×10^4 km s^{-1}. Then using Equation 5b, distance to galaxy = speed of galaxy/Hubble constant, the distance may be calculated as: distance = 3.6×10^4 km s^{-1}/72 km s^{-1} Mpc^{-1} = 500 Mpc.

Chapter 4

Question 12

(a) 230 °C is equivalent to about 500 K (since 273 + 230 is about 500). From Figure 27 it can be estimated that an object at a temperature of 500 K would radiate a black-body spectrum whose peak intensity occurs in the infrared region of the electromagnetic spectrum.

(b) From Figure 27 it may be estimated that an object whose black-body spectrum has a peak intensity in the ultraviolet part of the electromagnetic spectrum must be at a temperature of between about 10^4 K and 10^6 K.

Question 13

(a) Gravitational interactions are clearly important here: the attraction of every atom in the child's body, by every atom in the rest of the Earth, is responsible for slowing down the ascent and speeding up the descent. During bouncing, electromagnetic interactions come into play: they are responsible for holding together the atoms that form the child and the trampoline, and for the chemical processes by which the child converts energy in its muscles to replenish losses due to friction.

(b) Electromagnetic interactions are involved in the flow of electric current and the conversion of its energy into light in the lamp. They also govern the propagation of the light and its absorption by your retina. However, the electricity may have been generated in a nuclear power station, where both strong and weak interactions are involved in the nuclear reactor, or in a hydroelectric power station, where gravitational energy of water is involved.

(c) As in (b), electromagnetic interactions are involved in the absorption of the radiation, and the subsequent chemical changes to the skin. The radiation was generated by electromagnetic processes in the Sun, but the ultimate power source was nuclear, involving both strong and weak interactions. Gravitational interactions hold the Sun together and hold the bather on the beach.

(d) Chemotherapy, as the name suggests, involves chemical processes, and hence the electromagnetic interactions of electrons. Radiotherapy may involve injecting radioactive 'tracers', entailing strong and weak interactions in nuclei.

[Don't worry if you didn't identify the subsidiary interactions in each case.]

Chapter 5

Question 14

Before the work of Maxwell, Coulomb had shown that stationary electric charges give rise to electric forces, and Oersted and Ampère had shown that moving electric charges (currents) give rise to magnetic forces. Faraday and Henry had also shown that a changing magnetic force produces an electric force. Maxwell's predictions were that a changing electric force gives rise to a magnetic force and that, as a result electromagnetic waves must exist that travel at the speed of light.

Question 15

(a) An energy of 1 MeV (= 10^6 eV) implies that the maximum time by which the energy debt must be repaid is given by $(4 \times 10^{-15}$ eV s$)/(10^6$ eV$) = 4 \times 10^{-21}$ s. (This is an incredibly short time-scale — it is only a few thousandths of a billionth of a billionth of a second!)

(b) The energy debt could be repaid by the electron and positron annihilating each other.

Chapter 6

Question 16

To get four jets of hadrons, we need the radiation of two gluons. By analogy with the example in the question, this decreases the probability by a factor α_s squared or $(0.1 \times 0.1) = 10^{-2}$, at an energy of 100 GeV.

Question 17

Table 12 is the completed version of Table 8. Only particles with non-zero electric charge interact with photons. Only particles with colour charge interact with gluons.

Table 12   Completed version of Table 8.

Particle	Electric charge	Colour charge	Quanta with which the particle interacts
electron	−1	–	photons
electron neutrino	0	–	–
up quark	+2/3	red, green or blue	photons, gluons
down quark	−1/3	red, green or blue	photons, gluons
photon	0	–	–
gluon	0	colour and anticolour	gluons

Chapter 7

Question 18

(a) As shown by the Feynman diagram in Figure 80a, beta-plus decay involves an up quark (u) changing into a down quark (d), at A, where a W$^+$ boson is created. Shortly thereafter, the energy account is balanced, at B, by the production of a positron (e$^+$) and an electron neutrino (ν_e).

The electric charge initially is that of an up quark, i.e. +2/3 unit. The products of the decay are a down quark (electric charge, −1/3 unit), a positron (electric charge, +1 unit) and an electron neutrino (electric charge, 0). The net electric charge after the decay is therefore −1/3 + 1 = +2/3 unit, the same as it was initially. Electric charge is therefore conserved.

There is one quark present both before and after the decay, so the total number of quarks minus the number of antiquarks is conserved, and equal to one. There are no leptons present initially, but one lepton (the electron neutrino) and one antilepton (the positron) present at the end. Therefore the total number of leptons minus the number of antileptons is also conserved, and equal to zero.

(b) The Feynman diagram in Figure 80b shows how a W$^+$ boson is involved in the decay of an antimuon. At A the antimuon (μ^+) decays to a W$^+$ boson and a muon antineutrino ($\bar{\nu}_\mu$), then at B the W$^+$ boson decays into a positron (e$^+$) and an electron neutrino (ν_e).

The electric charge initially is that of an antimuon, i.e. +1 unit. The products of the decay are a positron (electric charge, +1 unit), a muon antineutrino (electric charge, 0) and an electron neutrino (electric charge, 0). The net electric charge after the decay is therefore +1 unit, the same as it was initially. Electric charge is therefore conserved.

There are no quarks or antiquarks involved in this decay, so the number of quarks is conserved, and equal to zero. There is one antilepton present initially (the antimuon), and two antileptons (the positron and muon antineutrino) plus one lepton (the electron neutrino) present at the end. Therefore the total number of leptons is also conserved, and equal to minus one (i.e. one antilepton).

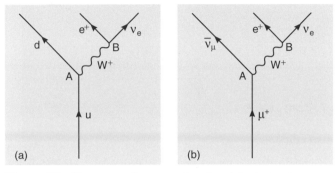

(a)   (b)

Figure 80 Feynman diagrams showing (a) a beta-plus decay process in which an up quark converts into a down quark, and (b) the decay of an antimuon.

Question 19

The strength of the electromagnetic interaction *increases* with increasing energy. At low energies (well below 1 GeV) it is characterized by $\alpha_{em} = 1/137$, at 100 GeV its strength increases to $\alpha_{em} = 1/128$.

The strength of the strong interaction *decreases* with increasing energy. At 1 GeV it is characterized by $\alpha_s = 0.4$ (from Figure 45) whereas at 100 GeV its strength has fallen to $\alpha_s = 0.1$.

The strength of the weak interaction *increases* with increasing energy. At 100 GeV its strength is comparable to that of the electromagnetic interaction, $\alpha_w = 10^{-2}$, whereas at an energy of 1 GeV, it is a factor of 10^8 smaller, $\alpha_w = 10^{-10}$.

Chapter 8

Question 20

Two phenomena that provide evidence for the curvature of space in the vicinity of massive objects are: (i) the bending of the path of radio waves emitted by distant quasars as the radio waves pass close to the Sun, and

(ii) gravitational lensing of quasars into multiple images as their light passes by intervening galaxies that lie along our line of sight.

Question 21

Newton's law of gravity was phrased in terms of a force between massive particles. A quantum theory of gravity will describe gravitational interactions in terms of the exchange of gravitons.

Chapter 9

Question 22

(a) Only the first step of the reaction chain depends on the weak interaction. The weak interaction allows one type of quark to convert into another when W bosons are emitted. In Step 1, two protons are fused together to make a deuterium nucleus consisting of one proton and one neutron, with the emission of a positron and a neutrino. The net effect is that a proton has been converted into a neutron, a positron and a neutrino. At a deeper level, an up quark transforms into a down quark and emits a W^+ boson. This then decays into a positron and an electron neutrino. As you saw in Chapter 7, this involves the weak interaction.

(b) All three steps in the reaction chain rely on the strong interaction. In each case, positively charged particles (protons and nuclei) are fused together. This entails that their electrical repulsion be overcome, and the residual strong interaction that operates inside nuclei is the only one of the four fundamental interactions which is able to do this.

Question 23

(a) In the case of free–free emission, the change in energy of the electron can take *any* value, up to the kinetic energy that the electron initially possesses. So, the photon emitted in the process can similarly have any energy. By contrast, in bound–bound emission, only certain energy levels are allowed for the atom. So the photon emitted can have only certain specific energies.

(b) Summing over many such events, the first process would give rise to a continuous spectrum of photon energies, whereas the second process would give rise to an emission line spectrum.

Question 24

(a) When an electron neutrino interacts with a deuterium nucleus, the process relies on the weak interaction. At a nuclear level, the neutrino splits the deuterium nucleus apart, releasing two protons and an electron. In symbols:

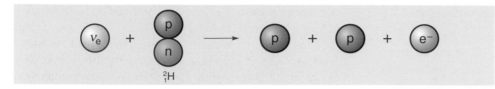

(b) Alternatively, at the level of nucleons, the neutron in the deuterium nucleus is converted into a proton, and an electron is emitted. The process may therefore be represented as:

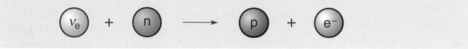

(c) Since a neutron has the quark composition (udd) whereas a proton has the composition (uud), the neutrino interaction may be considered at a more fundamental level. The neutrino interacts with a down quark in the neutron, to create an up quark and an electron. In symbols:

Chapter 10

Question 25

(a) The completed Table 11 is shown in Table 13.

Table 13   Completed version Table 11. Quanta involved in electroweak unification.

Quanta	Mass energy/GeV
photon	0
W$^+$ boson	80
W$^-$ boson	80
Z^0 boson	90
Higgs boson	1000

(b) The photon is the only one that is massless. As a consequence of this, Coulomb's law is an inverse square law of force with a very large range. Conversely, W and Z bosons do have mass and so have only a very short range.

Question 26

(a) About 12 orders of magnitude span the more or less reliable parts of the story: from the 1 eV energy transfers in hydrogen atoms, to the 10^{12} eV (10^3 GeV) investigated at existing or planned particle accelerators.

(b) A further 12 orders of magnitude remain in the range up to a notional scale of 10^{24} eV (10^{15} GeV) conjectured for grand unification.

Question 27

(a) Higgs bosons, (b) X bosons, (c) strings and branes.

Chapter 11

Question 28

Feynman diagrams for these decay processes are shown in Figure 81.

(a) Figure 81a shows the decay of a charm quark into a strange quark and a W$^+$ boson, which in turn decays into a positron and an electron neutrino.

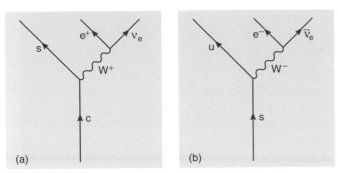

Figure 81 Feynman diagrams illustrating the decay of (a) a charm quark and (b) a strange quark.

(b) Figure 81b shows the decay of a strange quark into an up quark and a W^- boson, which in turn decays into an electron and an electron antineutrino.

Question 29

If weak interactions did not exist in the hypothetical Universe, and if only up quarks, down quarks, electrons, electron neutrinos and their antiparticles were initially present:

- Conversions between protons and neutrons would be impossible.

- As protons cannot convert into neutrons, there would be no proton–proton chain of nuclear fusion in stars (including the Sun).

- As primordial neutrons cannot convert into protons, there would be equal numbers of protons and neutrons in the Universe.

- As there are equal numbers of primordial protons and neutrons, these would all combine (eventually) to form nuclei of helium-4. Consequently there would be no hydrogen in the Universe.

- As there is no hydrogen in the Universe, there would be no water, no organic chemicals, and therefore no life as we know it.

Question 30

In principle, you could combine ^2_1H with ^3_2He, or you could combine a proton with ^4_2He. Both of these would give a nucleus consisting of three protons and two neutrons: ^5_3Li. (In practice this is unstable as it has too many protons, and splits apart into ^4_2He plus a proton.) Alternatively, you might try adding a free neutron to a ^4_2He nucleus to make ^5_2He. (However, this too is unstable as it contains too many neutrons, and splits apart.)

Question 31

(a) Nucleosynthesis — the formation of nuclei — occurred in the early Universe, between about 100 and 1000 seconds after the Big Bang. During this epoch, only low-mass nuclei, such as deuterium, helium and lithium were formed. A second site for nucleosynthesis is in the heart of stars, such as the Sun. Here, hydrogen undergoes nuclear fusion to form helium, and later on helium can fuse to form carbon, oxygen, silicon and other (relatively) low-mass nuclei. In fact, most nuclei below a mass number of about 62 (nuclei up to iron, cobalt and nickel) can form in the heart of stars in this way. Finally, nucleosynthesis can occur at the end of a star's life during a supernova explosion. In this process, many nuclei more massive than iron are formed and thrown violently out into the Universe, where they can be incorporated into future generations of stars and planets.

(b) (i) Most of the helium nuclei were formed during the primordial nucleosynthesis, soon after the Big Bang.

(ii) Most of the oxygen nuclei were formed in the heart of stars.

(iii) All the uranium nuclei were formed as a result of supernova explosions.

Question 32

Perhaps the simplest way to decide in which order a sequence of events occurred is to think about the energy required for each process. If the processes are then arranged in descending order of energy, they will automatically be in a time-ordered sequence.

Clearly, the formation of the fundamental constituents of matter, quarks and leptons, require the most energy of these processes. This event must have occurred first. Next, as the energy dropped, quarks and antiquarks would have mutually annihilated, leaving behind the relatively few residual matter particles from which to construct the material content of the Universe. Protons and neutrons form next, from the residual quarks. When neutrinos cease to interact with matter, the equilibrium conversion between protons and neutrons effectively stops. After this, the electrons and positrons mutually annihilate, leaving relatively few electrons to balance the charge of the protons. From this point on, light nuclei are able to form from the protons and neutrons available. Atoms form next from the nuclei and electrons that now constitute the matter content of the Universe. Finally, background photons interact for the last time with matter when the Universe is about 300 000 years old.

The sequence of the processes listed in the question is therefore:

(iii) formation of quarks and leptons

(vi) annihilation of quarks and antiquarks

(iv) formation of protons and neutrons

(vii) neutrinos cease to interact with matter or radiation

(v) annihilation of electrons and positrons

(ii) formation of light nuclei

(i) formation of atoms

(viii) background photons cease to interact with matter

Question 33

A summary of the contents of the Universe at the times indicated is shown in Table 14.

Question 34

The three key pieces of observational evidence for the hot big bang are:

the Hubble relationship linking the speed and distance of distant galaxies;

the cosmic microwave background radiation;

the relative abundances of helium, lithium and other light elements.

The first galaxies formed when the Universe was at least a few hundred thousand years old, and possibly much later. So, in theory, observations of distant galaxies only allow cosmologists to reach back this far in time.

The cosmic background radiation last interacted with matter when the Universe was about 300 000 years old. So observations of it only let cosmologists investigate conditions at that epoch.

It is the relative abundances of the light elements that allow cosmologists to reach back the furthest. These elements were formed when the Universe was between 100 and 1000 seconds old, and the reactions that created them were sensitive to things like the ratio of neutrons to protons, which were determined even earlier.

Chapter 12

Question 35

A closed Universe is finite in size and will eventually stop expanding. From here on a closed Universe will contract, ultimately reaching a Big Crunch, or a Big Bounce in which the whole sequence repeats. An open Universe is infinite in size and will carry on expanding forever.

Question 36

In 1998, astronomers reported measurements of 42 distant type Ia supernovae. These distant supernovae are about 15–25% *fainter* than they ought to be if the Universe had simply followed the expansion rate predicted by the conventional flat Universe model. The proposal is that the light from the supernova explosions has travelled a greater distance than is predicted by the conventional model because the Universe's expansion has *accelerated* whilst the light was on its way to the Earth.

Table 14 The contents of the Universe at various times.

Section	Time/s	Contents of the Universe
11.2 The very early Universe	10^{-36}	Six flavours of quark, six flavours of lepton, X bosons, photons (and presumably gluons, gravitons, W and Z bosons too).
11.3 Inflation	10^{-32}	The same as above, except that X bosons had largely disappeared.
11.4 The quark–lepton era	10^{-5}	Up and down quarks, electrons, positrons, neutrinos and antineutrinos, photons.
11.5 The hadron era	100	protons, neutrons, electrons, neutrinos and antineutrinos, photons.
11.6 Primordial nucleosynthesis	1000	Mainly hydrogen and helium-4 nuclei; traces of deuterium, helium-3, and lithium-7; electrons, neutrinos and antineutrinos, photons.
11.7 Structure in the Universe	today	Galaxies, stars, gas and dust (all of which are made of atoms, the vast majority of which are hydrogen and helium); photons (cosmic microwave background) fill all space; neutrinos and antineutrinos still present but almost undetectable.

Question 37

Type Ia supernovae are believed to be the result of white dwarfs being pushed over the Chandrasekhar limit of $1.4M_\odot$. Since they all result from the same mass of star exploding, they should all have the same luminosity.

Question 38

(a) Luminous matter is the material in the Universe that we can actually see with telescopes. It is made up of familiar protons, neutrons and electrons and constitutes the galaxics, stars, gas and dust that we 'see' as a result of the light and other electromagnetic radiation they emit. It probably constitutes about 0.5% of the critical density.

(b) Baryonic dark matter is invisible, but it too is probably made up of protons, neutrons and electrons. It is dark because it emits no light, or other radiation. It is thought to exist in the outer regions (or halos) of galaxies and may be made up of 'dead stars' that were never able to undergo nuclear fusion. These dead stars are referred to as MaCHOs. They probably constitute about 4% of the critical density.

(c) Non-baryonic dark matter is the matter that is predicted to exist if the Universe really does have a critical density. It cannot be made up of familiar protons, neutrons and electrons. Not only is it invisible, but we have no real idea what it is made of. These unknown particles are called WIMPs. They probably constitute about 23% of the critical density.

(d) Dark energy is the name given to a mysterious form of 'negative gravity' that opposes the normal gravitational attraction between massive objects. It manifests its presence via the cosmological constant (lambda) and can be quantified in terms of 'omega lambda' — the density of dark energy in the Universe. It probably constitutes about 73% of the critical density.

Question 39

In the cyclic ekpyrotic Universe model, non-baryonic dark matter is explained as matter on the hidden brane that interacts with matter on the visible brane (i.e. in our Universe) through gravitational interactions that act through the fifth dimension. Dark energy is explained as due to the vacuum that exists between the hidden brane and the visible brane.

Question 40

In the cyclic ekpyrotic Universe model there have been an infinite number of cycles stretching away into the past, each of which originated with the collision of two branes. The age of the Universe is therefore infinite. Each cycle initiates a new phase of expansion of the Universe on the visible brane. Since there have been an infinite number of these cycles, the size of the Universe is also infinite.

Key relationships

energy of photon = energy of upper energy level − energy of lower energy level   (1)

brightness is proportional to luminosity divided by distance squared   (2)

redshift = change in wavelength/original wavelength   (3)

speed of galaxy = redshift × speed of light   (4)

speed of galaxy = Hubble constant × distance to galaxy   (5)

mean photon energy in electronvolts = temperature in kelvin/3000   (6)

Glossary

Cross-references to other Glossary entries are indicated by underlining.

absolute temperature scale   Also known as the kelvin scale. A temperature scale for which the zero corresponds to the lowest possible temperature, absolute zero. The unit of temperature on this scale is the kelvin, abbreviated as K. To convert a temperature on the absolute scale into a temperature on the celsius scale, you subtract 273 from the numerical value of the temperature in kelvin.

absorption line   A spectral line produced when atoms of a particular type absorb photons with a particular energy.

absorption spectrum   A spectrum containing absorption lines. If a substance is illuminated with white light, then its absorption spectrum will consist of a continuous spectrum on which dark lines are superimposed.

acceleration (of the Universe)   A possible effect whereby the rate of overall expansion of space may be increasing as a result of the effect of dark energy. (See also deceleration.)

annihilation   The process whereby a matter particle combines with its antimatter counterpart to produce photons of electromagnetic radiation. The mass of the matter and antimatter particles is converted into energy. For example, when a slowly moving electron annihilates with a slowly moving positron, the total mass of the two particles is converted into a pair of gamma-ray photons, each of which has an energy of about 500 keV. The opposite process is referred to as pair creation.

antibaryon   A subatomic particle composed of three antiquarks. The antimatter counterpart of a baryon. A type of hadron. Examples include the antiproton and antineutron.

antielectron   See positron.

antilepton   A fundamental particle, the antimatter counterpart of a lepton. There are six flavours of antilepton: the antielectron (or positron e⁺), the antimuon (μ⁺), the antitauon (τ⁺), the electron antineutrino ($\bar{v}_e$), the muon antineutrino ($\bar{v}_\mu$), and the tauon antineutrino ($\bar{v}_\tau$).

antimatter   Every type of matter particle has a corresponding type of antimatter particle which has the same mass but opposite other properties, such as electric charge.

antimuon (μ⁺)   A fundamental particle (an antilepton) with electric charge +1 unit which is similar to a positron but with a mass about 200 times heavier. Its corresponding matter particle is called the muon (μ⁻).

antineutrino ($\bar{v}$)   Any one of the electron antineutrino, muon antineutrino, or tauon antineutrino. They all have zero electric charge.

antiquark   A fundamental particle, the antimatter counterpart of a quark. There are six flavours of antiquarks: antiup ($\bar{u}$), antidown ($\bar{d}$), anticharm ($\bar{c}$), antistrange ($\bar{s}$), antitop ($\bar{t}$), and antibottom ($\bar{b}$). Antiquarks are found in antibaryons and mesons.

antitauon (τ⁺)   A fundamental particle (an antilepton) with electric charge +1 unit, which is similar to a positron but with a mass about 3500 times heavier. Its corresponding matter particle is called the tauon (τ⁻).

atom   The smallest entity of a chemical element. An atom consists of a positively charged nucleus surrounded by a cloud of one or more negatively charged electrons.

atomic number   The number of protons within the nucleus of an atom. It is also equal to the number of electrons in the neutral atom. Each chemical element has a unique, characteristic atomic number.

atomic spectra   Emission spectra or absorption spectra characteristic of particular atoms.

baryon   A subatomic particle composed of three quarks. The matter counterpart of an antibaryon. A type of hadron. Examples include the proton and neutron.

baryonic dark matter   Dark matter composed of the familiar protons, neutrons and electrons. See MaCHOs. (See also non-baryonic dark matter)

beta-minus decay   A type of nuclear decay in which a neutron is converted into a proton with the emission of an electron and an electron antineutrino. At a deeper level this may be understood as resulting from the conversion of a down quark into an up quark. All beta-decays are examples of processes that depend on the weak interaction.

beta-plus decay   A type of nuclear decay in which a proton is converted into a neutron with the emission of a positron and an electron neutrino. At a deeper level this may be understood as resulting from the conversion of an up quark into a down quark. All beta-decays are examples of processes that depend on the weak interaction.

Big Bang   The event which is believed to mark the origin of time and space. Consequences of the Big Bang include the fact that <u>space</u> is expanding, that the <u>temperature</u> of the Universe is falling and that elements such as <u>helium</u>, <u>lithium</u> and <u>deuterium</u> have certain abundances in the Universe.

Big Bounce   In a <u>closed Universe</u>, it is possible that a <u>Big Crunch</u> is followed by a Big Bounce leading to a succession of expansion and contraction phases.

Big Clap   In the <u>ekpyrotic Universe</u> model, the collision of two <u>branes</u> is described as a Big Clap, and gives rise to the traditional <u>Big Bang</u>.

Big Crunch   In a <u>closed Universe</u>, the expansion will eventually become a contraction, leading to a Big Crunch in which the events of the <u>Big Bang</u> follow in reverse order.

billion   Meaning 10^9 or a thousand million.

black-body spectrum (or <u>thermal spectrum</u>)   A <u>continuous spectrum</u> emitted by an object in <u>thermal equilibrium</u>. All black-body spectra have a similar characteristic shape whose mean <u>photon</u> <u>energy</u> is uniquely related to the <u>temperature</u> of the object (or equivalently the temperature of the radiation).

black-body radiation   The <u>electromagnetic radiation</u> that comprises a <u>black-body spectrum</u>.

black hole   The ultimate condensed state of matter. A black hole has such a strong gravitational pull that not even light can escape from it. Black holes with a mass similar to that of the Sun may form as the end-point of stars of very high mass (see <u>neutron star</u> for comparison.) Black holes with a mass up to a billion times that of the Sun probably exist in the centre of many galaxies.

blueshift   The shift in the <u>spectrum</u> of a source of <u>electromagnetic radiation</u> that is approaching the observer. Equal to the shift in <u>wavelength</u> of a particular feature in the spectrum divided by the original (or rest) wavelength of the same feature. A blueshift corresponds to a *shortening* of the emitted wavelength.

boson   A particle responsible for transmitting one of the <u>four fundamental interactions</u>, or one of the unified interactions. See <u>photon</u>, <u>gluon</u>, <u>W boson</u>, <u>Z boson</u>, <u>graviton</u>, <u>Higgs boson</u>, <u>X boson</u>.

bottom (quark) (b)   A fundamental particle with <u>electric charge</u> −1/3 unit.

bound–bound absorption   A process in which an <u>atom</u> (or other <u>quantum system</u>) absorbs a <u>photon</u> of <u>electromagnetic radiation</u> and so makes a <u>transition</u> from one bound <u>quantum state</u> to another bound quantum state of higher <u>energy</u>.

bound–bound emission   A process in which an <u>atom</u> (or other <u>quantum system</u>) emits a <u>photon</u> of <u>electromagnetic radiation</u> and so makes a <u>transition</u> from one bound <u>quantum state</u> to another bound quantum state of lower <u>energy</u>.

bound–free absorption   A process in which an <u>atom</u> (or other <u>quantum system</u>) absorbs a <u>photon</u> of <u>electromagnetic radiation</u> and so makes a <u>transition</u> from a bound <u>quantum state</u> to a quantum state in which an electron is freed from the atom. Also referred to as <u>ionization</u>.

brane   A hypothetical construct in 11-dimensional space that is the fundamental component in <u>M-theory</u>.

brightness   The amount of <u>light</u> (or other <u>electromagnetic radiation</u>) received from a source. It is related to the <u>luminosity</u> of the source and its distance away by the relationship: brightness is proportional to luminosity divided by distance squared. The brightness of a source is also referred to as its <u>flux</u> and may be measured in the unit watts per square metre.

bulk brane   In the <u>ekpyrotic Universe</u> model, the bulk brane peels off the <u>hidden brane</u> before colliding with the <u>visible brane</u> and giving rise to a <u>Big Clap</u>.

CERN   The European laboratory for particle physics near Geneva.

Chandrasekhar limit   The upper limit for the mass of a <u>white dwarf</u>, about 1.4 times the mass of the Sun. If a white dwarf accretes enough material to exceed this mass it may undergo a <u>type Ia supernova</u> explosion and collapse further to form a <u>neutron star</u>.

charge   See <u>electric charge</u> and <u>colour charge</u>.

charm (quark) (c)   A fundamental particle with <u>electric charge</u> +2/3 unit.

chemical compound   A substance comprising <u>atoms</u> of more than one type. An example is common salt, or sodium chloride, which contains atoms of sodium and chlorine arranged in a rigid structure.

closed Universe   A model of the <u>Universe</u> in which the density of matter is sufficient to eventually halt the <u>expansion</u> and cause a subsequent collapse into a presumed <u>Big Crunch</u>. A closed Universe is finite in size at all times. In a closed Universe, the actual density is greater than the <u>critical density</u>.

COBE   The cosmic background explorer satellite, which measured the cosmic microwave background radiation.

colour charge   A property possessed by quarks (and antiquarks) and gluons. It plays a role in QCD equivalent to that of electric charge in QED. Quarks can possess any one of red, green or blue colour charge, antiquarks can possess any one of antired, antigreen or antiblue colour charge. Like colour charges repel each other, unlike colour charges attract each other, via the strong interaction. Only colour-neutral particles can exist in isolation, all hadrons therefore have a net colour charge of zero. Hence baryons contain three quarks, each with a different colour charge (one red quark, one blue quark, one green quark), antibaryons contain three antiquarks, each with a different colour charge (one antired antiquark, one antiblue antiquark and one antigreen antiquark), and mesons contain a quark and an antiquark with opposite colour charges (either one red quark and one antired antiquark, or one blue quark and one antiblue antiquark, or one green quark and one antigreen antiquark).

confinement   The process by which quarks and antiquarks remain locked up inside hadrons.

continuous spectrum   A spectrum consisting of light (or other electromagnetic radiation) of *all* colours (or all energies or wavelengths). White light from a tungsten filament light bulb has a continuous spectrum.

continuum   The continuous band of energy levels that exist above the highest bound energy level in an atom. The continuum corresponds to quantum states in which the nucleus and electrons move around independently.

convection   Motion in a fluid as a consequence of temperature differences. Warmer portions of the fluid rise, transporting energy with them, and cooler portions sink.

cosmic microwave background (CMB)   The black-body radiation that pervades the entire Universe. It is a relic of the time when matter and electromagnetic radiation were last in thermal equilibrium, about 300 000 years after the Big Bang. The current temperature of the CMB is 2.73 K.

cosmological constant   A constant (lambda: Λ) introduced into the equations of general relativity by Albert Einstein to counteract the predicted expansion of the Universe. Now used to quantify the effect of dark energy.

cosmology   The study of the Universe as a whole, especially with regard to theories of its origin, nature, structure and evolution.

Coulomb's law   Two particles of unlike (or like) charge, at rest, will attract (or repel) each other with an electric force that is proportional to the product of the charges divided by the square of their separation.

critical density   The density that corresponds to a flat Universe model and characterised by omega (Ω) = 1. If the Hubble constant is currently 72 km s^{-1} Mpc^{-1}, then the critical density is equivalent to about four protons per cubic metre. The critical density may comprise about 73% from dark energy and 27% from luminous matter and dark matter.

dark energy   A mysterious form of 'negative gravity', which may constitute about 73% of the critical density of the Universe and be responsible for the acceleration of the expansion of the Universe. See also cosmological constant.

dark matter   Matter that cannot be seen but which makes its presence felt by the gravitational influence it has on other objects in the Universe. Baryonic dark matter (also known as MaCHOs) probably constitutes about 4% of the critical density whereas non-baryonic dark matter (also known as WIMPs) probably constitutes about 23% of the critical density (See also luminous matter and missing mass.)

deceleration   The term used to describe the slowing down of the expansion of the Universe, due to the gravitational attraction between all the matter in the Universe.

deuterium   Also known as 'heavy hydrogen'. An isotope of hydrogen, the nucleus of which contains one proton and one neutron. Compare with tritium.

dimensionless number   A number that has no unit. For example, the fine structure constant (α_{em}) and pi (π).

diffraction grating   A device consisting of many parallel, equally spaced apertures, very close together, used to diffract light. A diffraction grating may be characterized by the number of lines per millimetre, or by the line spacing.

dimension   The familiar Universe around us is seen to consist of four dimensions: three of space and one of time. String theory predicts that a further six dimensions are curled up very small. The ekpyrotic Universe theory predicts that another spatial dimension exists, separating the visible brane on which our Universe sits, from a hidden brane. Only gravity operates through this hidden dimension. All 11 dimensions may be understood within M-theory.

Doppler effect   The process by which the wavelength of a wave is altered when the source of the wave is moving with respect to the observer. Motion away from an observer causes the wavelength to be perceived as longer than that with which it was emitted; motion towards an observer causes the wavelength to be perceived as shorter than that with which it was emitted.

down (quark) (d)   A fundamental particle with electric charge –1/3 unit. One of the constituent particles of both the proton and the neutron.

ekpyrotic Universe   A model for the origin of the Universe in which successive collisions between branes each give rise to a Big Clap, and produce the enormous amount of heat that is required to understand the conventional Big Bang.

electric charge   A fundamental property of matter. There are two types, known as positive and negative charge. Like charges repel each other with an electric force, and unlike charges attract each other. Objects with no charge, or with equal amounts of positive and negative charge, are electrically neutral.

electrical energy   Potential energy that an object has because it is electrically charged and separated from other electrically charged objects.

electric force   The force produced by a stationary electric charge or by a varying magnetic force. (See also Coulomb's law.)

electromagnetic interaction   One of the four fundamental interactions. In most situations it is adequately described by Maxwell's laws of electromagnetism. However, by incorporating the effects of quantum physics and Einstein's special theory of relativity, the modern theory of QED provides a better description on very small size scales and in high-energy situations. It explains interactions between particles that possess electric charge in terms of the exchange of quanta called photons. It unifies all electric, magnetic and radiation phenomena into a single theory. Electromagnetic interactions are characterized by the dimensionless number referred to as the fine structure constant (α_{em}). Electromagnetic interactions get stronger with increasing energy of interaction. (Compare this behaviour with that of the strong interaction.)

electromagnetic radiation   The radiation given off by an electric charge whose speed or direction of motion changes, in accord with Maxwell's laws of electromagnetism. (Compare with gravitational radiation.)

electromagnetic spectrum   The entire range of phenomena ranging from radio waves, through microwaves, infrared radiation, light, unltraviolet radiation, and X-rays to gamma-rays. All electromagnetic radiation propagates as a wave with a speed $3 \times 10^8\,\mathrm{m\,s^{-1}}$, but interacts with matter (i.e. is emitted or absorbed) as a stream of particles, called photons.

electron (e^-)   A fundamental particle (a lepton) with electric charge −1 unit and mass energy about 500 keV. Electrons are produced in beta-minus decay processes. The antiparticle of the electron is known as the positron.

electron antineutrino ($\bar{v}_e$)   A fundamental particle (an antilepton) with zero electric charge. It is produced in beta-minus decay along with an electron. Its corresponding matter particle is the electron neutrino.

electron capture   A type of radioactive decay in which an atomic nucleus with too many protons captures an electron. The effect is for one proton to turn into a neutron with the emission of an electron neutrino. The effect on the nucleus is the same as beta-plus decay.

electron degeneracy pressure   An effect of quantum physics that provides the support against gravity in a white dwarf star.

electron neutrino (v_e)   A fundamental particle (a lepton) with zero electric charge. It is produced in beta-plus decay along with a positron. Its antiparticle is the electron antineutrino.

electron probability cloud   In some sense the electrons in an atom are actually in many places at once, and all that can be said is that there is a certain probability of each electron being in a particular location with a particular speed at a certain time. An electron probability cloud represents this probability pictorially. The cloud is dense in those regions where an electron has a high probability of being found, and sparse in those regions where it has a low probability of being found.

electron scattering   The process by which a free electron and a photon interact. Usually the photon will initially have more energy than the electron, and the result of the scattering is that the electron gains energy and the photon loses energy.

electronvolt (eV)   A unit of energy corresponding to the energy gained by an electron in passing from one terminal of a one volt battery to the other. The energies of photons of light are conveniently expressed in electronvolts.

electro-weak interaction   The name given to the combined electromagnetic interaction and weak interaction that is in evidence at energies greater than about 1000 GeV.

electroweak unification   The name given to the process whereby the electromagnetic interaction and the weak interaction become unified at energies of around 1000 GeV. Theories for this process predict that a so called Higgs boson will be in evidence at reactions occurring at this energy.

element   A substance that consists of only one type of atom. For example, the chemical element copper is made only of copper atoms. A chemical element cannot be broken down into simpler constituents by using chemical reactions. All the atoms in a sample of a chemical element have the same atomic number.

emission line   A spectral line produced when atoms of a particular type emit photons with a particular energy.

emission spectrum   The spectrum of light produced by a vapour of atoms when excited by, for example, passage of an electric current. An emission spectrum contains emission lines of specific colours (corresponding to specific energies or wavelengths).

energy   A physical property possessed by an object. It measures the capacity of the object to make changes to other objects. There is a variety of possible changes, and these include changes in motion. Energy has various forms, including kinetic energy, gravitational energy and electrical energy, but the law of conservation of energy applies in all processes that involve conversions or transfers of energy.

energy level diagram   A pictorial way of representing energy levels. Energy levels corresponding to low energy are drawn at the bottom of the diagram.

energy levels   Specific values of energy that an atom (or other bound quantum system) is allowed to have. Transitions occur between energy levels, in the process of which photons are emitted or absorbed.

energy–time uncertainty relation   A consequence of the Heisenberg uncertainty principle. States that an amount of energy may be 'borrowed' for a short time provided that the energy deficit multiplied by the time interval is less than about 4×10^{-15} eV s. It allows electron–positron pairs to be created spontaneously inside atoms for a brief amount of time.

excited state   Any quantum state that is not the ground state.

exclusion principle   A rule of quantum physics, described by Wolfgang Pauli, which forbids any two electrons in the same atom from occupying the same quantum state.

expansion (of the Universe)   Referring to the fact that, on large scales, the separations of objects in the Universe are increasing. This is due to the fact that space itself is expanding. The rate of expansion may be subject to either a deceleration or an acceleration.

exponent   See index.

Feynman diagram   A pictorial way of representing reactions involving quarks, leptons and quanta, such as photons, gluons, W bosons and Z bosons. Mathematical expressions can be associated with each line or intersection in such a diagram to enable probabilities for different reactions to be calculated.

fine structure constant   A dimensionless number that characterizes the strength of the electromagnetic interaction. It has a value given by $\alpha_{em} = 1/137$ at low energies.

flat Universe   A model of the Universe in which the density of matter is exactly equal to the critical density. Such a Universe will continue expanding, but at an ever-decreasing rate. It will reach a zero rate of expansion only at an infinite time in the future. A flat Universe is infinite in size at all times. It is most probable that we live in a flat Universe.

flavour   Somewhat whimsical name used to describe the different types of lepton (i.e. electron, electron neutrino, muon, muon neutrino, tauon, tauon neutrino) and the different types of quark (up, down, strange, charm, top, bottom).

flavour oscillations   The mechanism by which neutrinos change into other types of neutrino. Believed to be the solution to the solar neutrino problem.

flux   See brightness.

four fundamental interactions   The electromagnetic interaction, the strong interaction, the weak interaction and the gravitational interaction, which are believed to be at the heart of all processes that occur in the Universe.

free–bound emission   A process in which a free electron (i.e. one not bound to a nucleus in an atom or ion) becomes bound to a nucleus. In the process the electron loses energy and emits a photon of electromagnetic radiation. Also referred to as recombination.

159

free–free absorption   A process in which a free electron (i.e. one not bound to a nucleus in an atom or ion) absorbs a photon of electromagnetic radiation and so gains energy. The photon disappears in the process and the electron remains free after the event.

free–free emission   A process in which a free electron (i.e. one not bound to a nucleus in an atom or ion) emits a photon of electromagnetic radiation and so loses energy, but remains free after the event. The usual way in which this happens is when an electron changes its speed or direction of motion when passing close to a positively charged particle, such as a nucleus.

galaxy   An ensemble of stars, gas and dust. Our own galaxy, the Milky Way, is a typical spiral galaxy with a mass about a hundred billion times that of the Sun.

general relativity   See general theory of relativity.

general theory of relativity   The description of the gravitational interaction given by Einstein. It is appropriate in situations where the masses involved are very large, or when massive objects undergo large changes in their speed or direction of motion. It predicts that massive objects whose speed or direction of motion changes rapidly will be a source of gravitational radiation.

generations (of fundamental particles)   The electron and electron neutrino are referred to as first-generation leptons; the up and down quarks are referred to as first-generation quarks. The muon, muon neutrino, strange and charm quarks belong to the second generation; the tauon, tauon neutrino, top and bottom quarks belong to the third generation.

gluon   The quantum of energy associated with the strong interaction. It plays a role in QCD analogous to that of photons in QED. Unlike photons, gluons experience the strong interaction (photons do not experience the electromagnetic interaction). This is because gluons possess colour charge (photons do not possess conventional electric charge). Consequently, gluons have a very short range and are never observed in isolation.

grand unification   The name given to the process whereby the electromagnetic interaction, the weak interaction and the strong interaction become unified at energies of around 10^{15} GeV. Theories for this process, known as grand unified theories or GUTs, predict that so-called X bosons will be in evidence at reactions occurring at this energy.

grand unified theory (GUT)   A theory expressing the grand unification of the electromagnetic interaction, the weak interaction and the strong interaction.

gravitational energy   Work has to be done against the gravitational force to raise an object to a greater height, and the energy transferred is stored as gravitational energy. This energy is released and can do work when the object falls. Gravitational energy is a form of potential energy. It is only *changes* of gravitational energy that are important in energy transfers and conversion.

gravitational force   The force produced by an object that possesses mass. (See also Newton's law of gravity.)

gravitational interaction   One of the four fundamental interactions. In most situations, the description of gravity provided by Newton's law of gravity is appropriate. However, when the masses involved are very large, or when massive objects undergo large changes in their speed or direction of motion, Einstein's general theory of relativity provides a better description. In the early Universe, when very small distance scales and enormous energy scales applied, a theory of quantum gravity is needed to provide a more appropriate description.

gravitational lensing   An effect of curved space predicted by general relativity whereby the light from a distant object, such as a quasar, is lensed by an intervening massive object, such as a galaxy, to create multiple images of the distant object.

gravitational radiation   The radiation given off by massive objects whose speed or direction of motion changes, in accord with Einstein's general theory of relativity. (Compare with electromagnetic radiation.)

graviton   The quantum of energy that is associated with the gravitational interaction. There is currently no experimental evidence for gravitons, but they are predicted to exist by any theory of quantum gravity. Gravitons themselves have no mass but would experience the gravitational interaction. (Compare this behaviour with photons and gluons, which also have no mass: photons do not experience the electromagnetic interaction, but gluons do experience the strong interaction.)

ground state   The quantum state that corresponds to the lowest energy level of an atom, or other quantum system.

hadron   A composite particle composed of quarks and/or antiquarks. Baryons are hadrons consisting of three quarks, antibaryons are hadrons consisting of three antiquarks, mesons are hadrons consisting of a quark and an antiquark.

helioseismology   The study of oscillations on the surface of the Sun, by which the interior structure, density and composition of the Sun may be determined.

helium   The second most abundant element in the Universe. Its nucleus consists of two protons and either one or two neutrons (in the isotopes helium-3 and helium-4, respectively). A neutral helium atom also contains two electrons.

hidden brane   In the ekpyrotic Universe model, the hidden brane is parallel to the visible brane on which our Universe sits, but is separated from it across the fifth dimension.

Higgs boson   A particle proposed to exist by current theories of electroweak unification. The Higgs boson is expected to have a mass energy of around 1000 GeV.

horizon distance   The limiting distance to which it is possible to observe objects in the Universe. It is due to the finite speed of light. Light (or other electromagnetic radiation) from objects more distant than this has simply not had time to reach us since the Universe began.

hot big bang   The name given to the theory that describes the origin and early evolution of the Universe. (See Big Bang.)

Hubble constant   The constant of proportionality in the Hubble relationship, which relates the recession speed of distant galaxies to their distance away. The current best estimate of the Hubble constant is about $72 \, \mathrm{km \, s^{-1} \, Mpc^{-1}}$. The Hubble constant was larger in the distant past than it is today.

Hubble relationship   Discovered by Edwin Hubble in 1929, the relationship expresses the fact that the farther away a galaxy is from us, the faster it is receding. It may be expressed as: speed of galaxy = Hubble constant × distance to galaxy.

hydrogen   The simplest and most abundant element in the Universe. A neutral hydrogen atom consists of a single proton and a single electron bound together. See also deuterium and tritium.

index   The power to which a number is raised. For example the expression 10^5 is read as 'ten to the power five' and means $10 \times 10 \times 10 \times 10 \times 10$. In this case, the index is '5'.

inflation   The name given to a theory that describes the behaviour of the Universe at times between about 10^{-35} s and 10^{-32} s after the Big Bang. During this interval it is proposed that distances within the Universe increased by an extraordinarily huge factor. Inflation is believed to be caused by the way in which the strong interaction and the electroweak interaction became distinct. If inflation is correct, it predicts that we live in a flat Universe.

inverse square law   Any equation in which the size of one quantity is inversely proportional to the square of another quantity. Coulomb's law, Newton's law of gravity, and the relationship between brightness and distance are all examples of inverse square laws. For example, the brightness of a 100 W light bulb seen from a distance of 300 m is *nine times less* than the brightness of a similar light bulb seen from a distance of 100 m. The former bulb is three times farther away, and so appears nine times (i.e. three squared) fainter.

ion   An atom that has lost (or gained) one or more electrons, leaving it with a positive (or negative) electric charge.

ionized   When one or more electrons are removed from an atom, the atom is said to be ionized.

ionization   The process by which an atom (or existing ion) is turned into an ion (or more positive ion) when one or more electrons are removed from it.

ionization energy   The energy required in order to ionize an atom, or to further ionize an existing ion.

isotope   Atoms with the same number of protons in their nuclei, but different numbers of neutrons, are called isotopes. Because they have the same number of protons, they have the same atomic number and are atoms of the same chemical element. But because of the different number of neutrons, they differ in mass number.

kinetic energy   Energy associated with motion of an object. Depends on the mass of the object and the speed at which it is moving.

LEP2   The large electron–positron collider mark 2, a particle accelerator at CERN.

lepton   A fundamental particle, the matter counterpart of an antilepton. There are six flavours of lepton: the electron (e^-), the muon (μ^-), the tauon (τ^-), the electron neutrino (ν_e), the muon neutrino (ν_μ), and the tauon neutrino (ν_τ).

LHC   The large hadron collider, a particle accelerator at CERN.

light   That part of the electromagnetic spectrum with wavelengths between about 400 nm (violet) and 700 nm (red).

light year   The distance travelled by a beam of light in one year. Equal to about 10^{13} km or one-third of a parsec.

look-back time   When observing distant galaxies, the light (and other electromagnetic radiation) that is measured has taken a significant amount of time to cross the intervening space between the galaxy and us. The look-back time quantifies how far into the past we are seeing when observing a particular distant galaxy.

luminosity   The amount of power emitted by a luminous object, such as a star or galaxy, in the form of light or other electromagnetic radiation. It is related to the observed brightness of an object by the relationship: luminosity is proportional to brightness multiplied by distance squared. Luminosity may be measured in the unit of watts.

luminous matter   Matter that can actually be seen as a result of the electromagnetic radiation it emits. Comprised of galaxies, stars, gas and dust and may constitute only about 0.5% of the critical density. (See also dark matter and missing mass.)

MaCHOs   Massive compact halo objects, postulated as existing in the outer haloes of galaxies and contributing to the baryonic dark matter they contain. They may consist of failed stars that were never able to ignite nuclear fusion in their cores.

magnetic force   The force produced by an electric current (i.e. a moving electric charge) or by a varying electric force.

mass   The amount of matter in an object. Mass determines the magnitude of the force of gravity acting on a body. This gravitational force is also known as the weight of the body. Mass and energy are related by Einstein's equation $E = mc^2$.

mass energy   The energy equivalent of the mass of a body according to Einstein's equation $E = mc^2$. For example, the mass energy of an electron is about 500 keV (0.5 MeV), and the mass energy of either a proton or neutron is about 1000 MeV (1 GeV).

mass number   The number of nucleons (protons and neutrons) in the nucleus of an atom.

matter–antimatter annihilation   See annihilation.

Maxwell's laws of electromagnetism   A theory unifying the phenomena of electric and magnetic interactions, as they were understood towards to the end of the 19th century. The theory explains that stationary electric charges give rise to electric forces, that moving electric charges (i.e. electric currents) give rise to magnetic forces, that a changing magnetic force produces an electric force, and that a changing electric force produces a magnetic force. A prediction of Maxwell's theory was the existence of electromagnetic radiation, which travels through space at the speed of light. (Compare with quantum electrodynamics.)

meson   A subatomic particle composed of a quark and an antiquark. A type of hadron. Examples of mesons include the pions.

missing mass   If we live in a flat Universe, then the amount of luminous matter that is observed (in the form of stars, galaxies, gas and dust) plus the amount of baryonic dark matter, is not sufficient to account for the critical density of matter that must exist in the Universe. The difference is described as missing mass and must be in the form of particles that are totally unlike the familiar protons, neutrons or electrons from which the rest of the Universe is composed. This is non-baryonic dark matter. Such particles are often described as WIMPs and may constitute about 23% of the critical density.

molecule   A group of atoms bound together. An example is the water molecule (H_2O).

M-theory   A candidate for a theory of everything. It incorporates all of the pre-existing versions of string theory, and proposes the existence of branes in 11 dimensions.

muon (μ^-)   A fundamental particle (a lepton) with electric charge −1 unit which is similar to an electron but with a mass about 200 times heavier. Its antiparticle is called the antimuon (μ^+).

muon antineutrino ($\bar{\nu}_\mu$)   A fundamental particle (an antilepton) with zero electric charge. Its corresponding matter particle is called the muon neutrino.

muon neutrino (ν_μ)   A fundamental particle (a lepton) with zero electric charge. Its antiparticle is called the muon antineutrino.

nanometre 10^{-9} of a metre. Different colours of visible light have different wavelengths of a few hundred nanometres.

neutrino (ν)   Any one of the electron neutrino, muon neutrino or tauon neutrino. They all have zero electric charge.

neutron (n)   One of the two types of particle found in the nucleus of an atom. Neutrons are baryons, with the quark composition (udd). They have an electric charge of zero, and a mass energy of about 1 GeV.

neutron degeneracy pressure   An effect of quantum physics that provides the support against gravity in a neutron star.

neutron star   When a high-mass star runs out of nuclear fuel, it will undergo a type II supernova explosion and its core will collapse to form a neutron star. A neutron star has a mass similar to that of the Sun, but a radius of only about 10 km. A neutron star is supported against gravity by an effect of quantum physics known as neutron degeneracy pressure. See also white dwarf and black hole.

Newton's law of gravity   Two particles attract each other with a gravitational force that is proportional to the product of the masses divided by the square of their separation.

non-baryonic dark matter   Dark matter not composed of the familiar protons, neutrons and electrons. See WIMPs. (See also baryonic dark matter)

nucleons   The protons and neutrons in the nucleus of an atom.

nucleosynthesis   The process by which the nuclei of elements (other than hydrogen) are formed. There are believed to be three sites (or epochs) where (or when) nucleosynthesis occurs (or has occurred). Light nuclei, such as deuterium, helium and lithium, were formed in the early Universe when the Universe was between about 100 s and 1000 s old. Nuclear fusion inside the cores of stars is responsible for the formation of more helium nuclei, and also for the formation of other nuclei up to those with a mass around that of iron. Supernova explosions are responsible for the formation of more massive nuclei.

nucleus   The core of an atom. It contains nearly all of the atomic mass and is positively charged. With the exception of the hydrogen nucleus which is a single proton, nuclei consist of protons and neutrons.

omega (Ω)   A symbol used to express the density of the Universe. The critical density is quantified by $\Omega = 1$ and may be composed of a matter contribution ($\Omega_M = 0.27$) and a dark energy contribution ($\Omega_\Lambda = 0.73$).

open Universe   A model of the Universe in which the density of matter is not sufficient to halt the expansion. An open Universe is infinite in size at all times and will expand forever. In an open Universe, the actual density is less than the critical density.

order of magnitude   The nearest power of ten when quantifying a numerical value.

pair creation   The spontaneous creation of a matter–antimatter pair of particles from pure energy, such as a photon of electromagnetic radiation. The opposite process is referred to annihilation. The energy of the photon is converted into the mass of the matter and antimatter particles. For example, a photon of energy greater than about 1 MeV can spontaneously create an electron–positron pair, each of which has a mass energy of about 500 keV.

parsec   An astronomical distance unit equal to about 3×10^{13} km or 3 light years.

particle physics   The study of the fundamental components of which the Universe is built, particularly with regard to theories of their nature and interactions.

photometer   A device attached to a telescope used to measure the brightness of astronomical objects.

photon   Particles of light or other electromagnetic radiation. Monochromatic light consists of photons that each have exactly the same amount of energy, called a quantum of energy. Therefore also, the quantum of energy associated with the electromagnetic interaction. Photons have no mass or electric charge and do not experience the electromagnetic interaction. (Compare this behaviour with that of gravitons and gluons, which also have no mass or electric charge; however, gravitons experience the gravitational interaction, and gluons experience the strong interaction.)

pi (π)   A dimensionless number obtained by dividing the circumference of a circle by its diameter. It has a value of 3.141 592 654 (to nine decimal places).

pions   Any one of three types of meson composed of up and down quarks and antiquarks.

Planck energy   A natural energy scale of the Universe, defined in terms of other physical constants. It has a value of about 10^{19} GeV. The energy at which superunification of the four fundamental interactions is believed to occur.

Planck length   A natural length scale of the Universe, defined in terms of other physical constants. It has a value of about 10^{-35} m. The distance that light could travel during the Planck time.

Planck time   A natural time-scale of the Universe, defined in terms of other physical constants. It has a value of about 5×10^{-44} s. When the Universe was this old, it is believed that the superunification of the four fundamental interactions broke down.

positron (e⁺)   The antimatter counterpart to the electron. It has an electric charge of +1 unit, but the same mass as the electron. It is produced in beta-plus decay processes.

potential energy   Energy that is stored, and which depends on the position of an object and not on its motion. So-called because the object has the potential to do work when its position changes. Gravitational energy and electrical energy are both forms of potential energy.

principle of the conservation of energy   The expression of the fact that energy cannot be created or destroyed but merely changed from one form to another.

probability   A measure of how likely is the occurrence of a particular event. The probability that a roll of a single die will turn up a '3' for instance is 1 in 6.

product   The result of multiplying two numbers together.

proportional to   Two quantities are said to be proportional to each other if, when the value of one is multiplied (or divided) by a certain amount, the value of the other also becomes multiplied (or divided) by the same amount. For example, the cost of petrol is proportional to the volume of petrol bought, so the cost of buying 50 litres of petrol is twice the cost of buying 25 litres of petrol, which is five times the cost of buying 5 litres. The volume of petrol divided by its cost has the same, constant, value however much petrol is involved.

proton (p)   One of the two types of particle found in the nucleus of an atom. Protons are baryons, with the quark composition (uud). They have an electric charge of +1 unit and a mass energy of about 1 GeV.

proton–proton chain   The sequence of nuclear fusion reactions by which hydrogen nuclei are converted into helium nuclei in the core of the Sun and other stars.

pulsar   A rapidly spinning neutron star. As the neutron star spins on its axis, beams of radio emission sweep around the sky like the light from a lighthouse. On Earth, these beams are detected as pulses of radio emission.

QCD   See quantum chromodynamics.

QED   See quantum electrodynamics.

quantum   (i) The amount of energy carried by a single photon of light or other electromagnetic radiation. (ii) Used to refer to any system in which energy levels exist, and which therefore emit or absorb quanta of light, and/or in which the constituent particles have indeterminate positions and speeds.

quantum chromodynamics (QCD)   The theory that describes the strong interaction. It explains these interactions as arising due to the exchange of gluons between particles that possess colour charge. (For comparison see quantum electrodynamics.)

quantum electrodynamics (QED)   The theory that describes the electromagnetic interaction. It supersedes Maxwell's laws of electromagnetism in situations where the size scales are very small and the energy scales very large. It incorporates ideas from both quantum physics and the special theory of relativity and explains the electromagnetic interaction as arising due to the exchange of photons between particles that possess electric charge. (For comparison see quantum chromodynamics.)

quantum gravity   A theory that would unify quantum physics with the gravitational interaction. No such theory yet exists, but any such theory would predict the existence of quanta called gravitons.

quantum physics   The theory and study of systems of particles that exhibit quantized energy levels, and indeterminate positions and speeds.

quantum state (or state for short)   A description of the properties of an atom or other quantum system. In general, each energy level of an atom will correspond to more than one quantum state.

quark   A fundamental particle, the matter counterpart of an antiquark. There are six flavours of quark: up (u), down (d) charm (c), strange (s), top (t), and bottom (b). Quarks are found in baryons and mesons but never in isolation.

quasar   A distant, highly luminous type of galaxy, which emits huge amounts of radio waves and other electromagnetic radiation. They appear as points of light, hence their name: quasi-stellar object.

quintessence   An alternative name for dark energy.

radio astronomy   The observation and interpretation of radio waves emitted by objects in the Universe.

random walk   A process whereby a particle moves from one location to another by means of a series of discrete steps. The direction and length of each step, and the speed with which it occurs are all random, but there is an overall preferred direction such that on average the particle will move slowly in a given direction.

ratio   The result of dividing one number by another.

recession speed   The speed with which a galaxy recedes (travels away) from the Earth.

recombination   (See free–bound emission).

redshift   The shift in the spectrum of a source of electromagnetic radiation that is receding away from the observer. Numerically equal to the shift in wavelength of a particular feature in the spectrum divided by the original (or rest) wavelength of the same feature. A redshift corresponds to a *lengthening* of the emitted wavelength. All distant galaxies (beyond the Local Group) exhibit redshifts, none exhibit blueshifts. This is evidence for the fact that space is expanding.

scientific notation   A style of writing a number in the form: (number between 1 and 10) $\times 10^{\text{index}}$. Any number may be written in scientific notation by the use of a positive or negative index. For example, the number 54321 in scientific notation is: 5.4321×10^4.

solar neutrinos   Neutrinos emitted by the Sun as a consequence of the nuclear reactions occurring in its core.

solar neutrino problem   The apparent deficit of solar neutrinos observed at the Earth compared with the number predicted to be emitted by the Sun. Solved by the realization that some of the electron neutrinos emitted by the Sun undergo flavour oscillations into muon neutrinos or tauon neutrinos as they travel through space.

space   A property of the Universe. Space itself is expanding with the consequence that distant galaxies all exhibit redshifts and therefore appear to be receding from us.

special relativity   See special theory of relativity.

special theory of relativity   Einstein's theory which describes the behavior of matter and electromagnetic radiation when the energy and speed are extremely large. One consequence of the theory is the equivalence between mass and energy expressed by $E = mc^2$.

spectral distribution   A graph showing how the intensity of a spectrum varies with photon energy or wavelength.

spectral line   An emission line or an absorption line. Indicates that photons of a certain specific energy are emitted (or absorbed) by a particular substance.

spectrometer   A device attached to a telescope and used to measure the spectrum of astronomical objects.

spectrum   A means of displaying the different colours of light (or types of other radiation) contained within a source of light (or other radiation). It indicates the intensity of light at each different wavelength. Spectra may be continuous, or may show emission lines and/or absorption lines.

speed   The rate at which a distance is travelled.

speed of light   The speed at which electromagnetic radiation travels through a vacuum. The value is $3 \times 10^8 \, \text{m s}^{-1}$.

standard candle   A source of electromagnetic radiation that has a particular luminosity. An example is the tenth brightest galaxy in a cluster of galaxies.

star   A ball of (mainly) hydrogen and helium that is undergoing nuclear fusion reactions in its core. The Sun is a typical star.

strange (quark) (s)   A fundamental particle with electric charge −1/3 unit.

string   A hypothetical description of particles at energies entailed by superunification. Strings exist in ten dimensions, six of which are curled up very small. Different vibration modes of the strings correspond to different masses, electric charge or colour charge, and so give rise to the variety of particles we see.

strong interaction   Fundamental interaction between quarks and antiquarks responsible for binding them together as triplets inside baryons and antibaryons, or as quark antiquark pairs inside mesons. A residual effect of the strong interaction is responsible for binding protons and neutrons together as nuclei. One of the four fundamental interactions, described by the modern theory of QCD. It describes interactions between particles that possess colour charge in terms of the exchange of quanta called gluons. Strong interactions are characterized by the dimensionless number referred to as α_s, which has a value of about 0.1 at an energy of 100 GeV. Strong interactions get weaker with increasing energy of interaction. (Compare this behaviour with the electromagnetic interaction.)

subatomic particles   Any of electrons, protons or neutrons that make up an atom.

sum   The result of adding two or more numbers together.

Sun   Our local star.

supernova   See type Ia supernova and type II supernova.

supernova remnant   The expanding cloud of gas produced by a supernova explosion.

superunification   The name given to the process whereby the electromagnetic interaction, the weak interaction, the strong interaction and the gravitational interaction become unified at energies of around 10^{19} GeV, the Planck energy. A current proposed superunified theory involves the description of particles as strings or branes rather than as points.

tauon (τ^-)   A fundamental particle (a lepton) with electric charge –1 unit which is similar to an electron but with a mass about 3500 times heavier. Its antiparticle is called the antitauon (τ^+).

tauon antineutrino ($\bar{\nu}_\tau$)   A fundamental particle (an antilepton) with zero electric charge. Its corresponding matter particle is called the tauon neutrino.

tauon neutrino (ν_τ)   A fundamental particle (a lepton) with zero electric charge. Its antiparticle is called the tauon antineutrino.

theory of everything   A sought-after theory that may unify all four fundamental interactions.

thermal equilibrium   A state in which an object is emitting and absorbing electromagnetic radiation at the same rate. As such it will maintain a constant temperature.

thermal spectrum   See black-body spectrum.

top (quark) (t)   A fundamental particle with electric charge +2/3 unit.

transition   The name given to the process by which an atom 'jumps' from one quantum state to another with the corresponding emission or absorption of a photon.

tritium   An isotope of hydrogen, the nucleus of which contains one proton and two neutrons. Compare with deuterium.

type Ia supernova   When a white dwarf star accretes enough material to push it over the Chandrasekhar limit of about 1.4 times the mass of the Sun, it is believed that it will undergo an explosion referred to as a type Ia supernova. The end result is an expanding cloud of gas, referred to as a supernova remnant, and possibly a neutron star or a black hole.

type II supernova   When a massive star reaches the end of its life, its core consists of iron nuclei and there are no further nuclear fusion reactions available to release energy and so support the star against gravity. The outer layers of the star collapse inwards and, on meeting the incompressible core, suddenly expand outwards in a vast explosion, referred to as a type II supernova. In the explosion, nucleosynthesis of elements heavier than iron occurs. Supernovae are responsible for distributing massive nuclei throughout the Universe, as the cloud of material expands forming a supernova remnant. The core left behind will form either a neutron star or a black hole.

uncertainty principle   A fundamental result of quantum physics, discovered by Werner Heisenberg, that rules out the possibility of combining definite knowledge of some quantities (such as position) with definite knowledge of certain other quantities (such as velocity). It also limits the accuracy with which certain quantities can be measured simultaneously.

Universe   The entirety of space and all the matter and electromagnetic radiation contained within it.

up (quark) (u)   A fundamental particle with electric charge +2/3 unit. One of the constituent particles of both the proton and the neutron.

visible brane   In the ekpyrotic Universe model, the visible brane contains our visible Universe and is parallel to the hidden brane, but is separated from it across the fifth dimension.

wave   A periodic, or regularly repeating, disturbance that transports energy from one place to another

wavelength   The distance between two similar points on a wave profile.

wave–particle duality   Used to describe the fact that electromagnetic radiation travels from place to place like a wave, but interacts with matter as if its composed of a stream of particles called photons.

W boson   One of the quanta of the weak interaction. W bosons come in two varieties, labelled W^+ and W^-, where the superscripts denote the electric charge of the particles. Both W bosons have a mass energy of about 80 GeV.

weak interaction   Fundamental interaction involving both quarks and leptons. One of the four fundamental interactions. It describes interactions between particles in terms of the exchange of quanta called W bosons and Z bosons. There is no structure that is bound together by a 'weak force'. Weak interactions are responsible for processes such as beta decay, in which quarks change flavour and lepton–antilepton pairs are produced.

weight   A physical property that quantifies the strength of the gravitational force acting on a body that has a certain mass.

white dwarf   When a low-mass star runs out of nuclear fuel, its core will collapse to form a white dwarf star. A white dwarf has a mass similar to that of the Sun, but a radius similar to that of the Earth. A white dwarf is supported against gravity by an effect of quantum physics known as electron degeneracy pressure. The maximum mass of a white dwarf is about 1.4 times the mass of the Sun, known as the Chandrasekhar limit. See also neutron star and black hole.

WIMPs   Weakly interacting massive particles, proposed as making up the missing mass of the Universe. They are referred to as non-baryonic dark matter and their nature is currently unknown.

WMAP   The Wilkinson Microwave Anisotropy Probe satellite, which measured the cosmic microwave background radiation.

X boson   The proposed quanta associated with the grand unified interaction. They are predicted to have mass energies of around 10^{15} GeV (corresponding to the energy at which grand unification occurs) and are responsible for turning quarks into leptons (and vice versa) and matter into antimatter (and vice versa).

Z boson   One of the quanta of the weak interaction. Z bosons are often labelled Z^0, where the superscript denotes that they have zero electric charge. Z bosons have mass energies of about 90 GeV.

Acknowledgements

Grateful acknowledgement is made to the following sources for permission to reproduce material in this course.

Cover and CD and DVD labels

Image © copyright CERN.

Figures

Figure 1: Courtesy of the W. M. Keck Observatory; *Figures 2 and 40*: Copyright © CERN; *Figure 7*: Gary Larson/Copyright © Chronicle Features/Far Works Inc.; *Figures 11a, b, d, e and 34:* © Science and Society Picture Library; *Figure 11c*: Copyright © Corbis/Bettmann; *Figure 11f*: Courtesy of Ullarwin Bilderdienst; *Figure 17*: Courtesy of NASA and AURA/STScI; *Figure 20*: Courtesy of Patrick Corvan, Armagh Planetarium; *Figure 28*: Corporate Archives/Lucent Technologies/ Bell Laboratories; *Figure 30*: Copyright © Photo Réunion des Musées Nationaux; *Figures 31a and 50*: Copyright © Mary Evans Picture Library; *Figure 31b*: © Science Photo Library; *Figure 33*: Copyright © National Portrait Gallery; *Figure 36*: By permission of the Master and Fellows of St. John's College, Cambridge; *Figures 42 and 51*: Courtesy of the Archives, California Institute of Technology; *Figure 56a*: Myers, S. T. et al. 'Quadruple lens system found in the gravitational lens survey', *The Astrophysical Journal,* Vol. 447, July 1995; *Figure 56b*: Impey, C. D. et al. 'Hubble Space Telescope observations of the gravitational lens system B1422 + 231', *The Astrophysical Journal,* Vol. 462, May 1996; *Figure 56c*: Wesley, N. et al. 'Unlensing multiple arcs in 0024 + 1654: reconstruction of the source image', *The Astrophysical Journal,* Vol. 461, April 1996. The American Astrophysical Society; *Figure 57*: Reprinted from Beatly, J. K. and Chaikin, A. (1990) *The New Solar System,* third edition, Copyright © Sky Publishing 1990; *Figure 71a*: NASA Goddard Space Flight Center/COBE Science Working Group; *Figure 71b*: Courtesy of NASA/WMAP Science Team; *Figure 72*: Courtesy of NOAO; *Figure 75*: Permutter, S. et al. 'Measurement of omega and lambda from 42 high-redshift supernovae', *The Astrophysical Journal,* Vol. 517, June 1999. The American Astrophysical Society; *Figure 76*: Copyright © 2000 Mark A. Garlick; *Figure 77*: NASA and A. Riess (STScI).

INDEX

Entries and page numbers in **bold type** refer to terms defined in the glossary. Where the page number is given in *italics*, the indexed information is given mainly, or wholly, in a figure or table.